1962

This book may be kept

FOURTEEN

A Way

of

Mercy

Mother Mary Catherine McAuley
Foundress, Sisters of Mercy

A Way of Mercy

Catherine McAuley's Contribution to Nursing

By

SISTER MARY BEATA BAUMAN
Sister of Mercy

VANTAGE PRESS   NEW YORK

WASHINGTON   CHICAGO   HOLLYWOOD

Nihil Obstat:

B. M. Blank, O.P.
Censor Deputatus

✠ John J. Mitty
Archiepiscopus

Imprimatur:

Die 24° februarii, 1958

TO OUR MOTHER OF MERCY
for the thousands of Sisters of Mercy
who, walking the WAY OF MERCY
with Mother Mary Catherine McAuley,
find Christ in and bring Him to their fellow men.

Every effort has been made to respect all rights and to obtain proper permissions for the material cited in this study. If any rights or courtesies have been overlooked, it is hoped that the interested persons will forgive this inadvertence.

FOREWORD

The corporal and spiritual works of mercy have been the glory of the Church through the centuries.

Mother Catherine McAuley, Foundress of the Sisters of Mercy, established as their purpose the visitation and care of the sick and the education of the poor. From Dublin, Ireland, her followers have spread their mercy throughout the world.

We are grateful to the author for this recent study of Mother McAuley. We are confident that this excellent presentation will benefit the Sisters, already so imbued with the spirit of their Foundress.

It will profit, likewise, the historian, who is ever anxious to preserve accurately the facts of an important event, which may be lost with the passing of time.

Finally, it will profit the faithful who are always inspired by the life, with its trials and triumphs, of a remarkable soul.

JOHN J. MITTY
Archbishop of San Francisco

28 February 1958

I look upon Miss McAuley as one selected by Heaven for some great work. Her heart overflows with the charity of Jesus, whose all-consuming love burns within her. No woman has ever accomplished more for suffering, sorrowful humanity.

Reverend Dr. Michael Blake

(From the dedication sermon on the occasion of the blessing of the chapel in the House of Mercy on Baggot Street in Dublin, Octave of the Ascension, June 4, 1829.)

CONTENTS

LIST OF ILLUSTRATIONS

A Way

of

Mercy

PROLOGUE

DURING the years 1778 to 1841 there lived in Dublin one whose work is being carried forward today by the second largest religious community of women. As a child and young woman she was to know comfortable circumstances, poverty, and wealth; and finally, voluntary poverty in religion for the love of Christ and His poor, upon whom she bestowed her riches. As Foundress of the Sisters of Mercy, she labored but a short span of ten years to lay deep the foundations of her work as educator, social welfare worker, and nurse. This person was Catherine McAuley, the first woman under religious auspices to be permitted, since the days of Reformation, to enter the public hospitals of the United Kingdom and care for the sick.

Much has been written about the Sisters of Mercy and the phenomenal growth of Mother McAuley's community. The Foundress has been extolled as educator and social worker. Her care of the sick is recognized as the origin of the hundreds of hospitals conducted by her sisters. But there is no one work which deals primarily with the truly pioneering aspect of Catherine McAuley's work. This study was undertaken to bring into relief her apostolate for the sick; to analyze the spirit which animated her in a service rightly making her a forerunner of modern nursing, or the Morning Star of a system of nursing which foreshadows that termed "modern;" and to summarize the nursing of Mother McAuley's followers in the Crimea and the expansion of their apostolate to the sick.

9

The most essential sources drawn upon to gather into compact form the materials relating to Catherine McAuley's devotion to the sick were the Constitutions of the Congregation, the letters written by the Foundress, the instructions which she gave to the early members of the community, and the retreat conferences which she gave to the postulants and novices, preparatory to their reception of the holy habit and the profession of vows. Certain memoirs written by the sisters and others who knew the Foundress were drawn upon, as were more recent biographies known for their authenticity. Medical histories and journals supplied information concerning the treatment of disease and the medical men with whom Mother McAuley was associated in the care of the sick. (These references are described in more detail in Appendix A.)

This motley collection of timeworn pages depicted Mother Catherine's story of pioneer beginnings in nursing from which later professional status would develop. Some readers may not accept the religious convictions of Catherine McAuley and still others may be unwilling to agree with the portrayal of the period in history in which she lived and which affected her followers. But students who are concerned with the dynamics of human relations will accede to culture and the social system a share in the ultimate emerging of the personality which was Mother McAuley's.

Originally presented as a research project in the writing of a thesis, there were adaptations and additions made for publication purposes. Some were of the opinion that the first chapter required for thesis writing would have limited general reader interest and for this reason it was omitted. But to satisfy those who did not wish to see sacrificed the related literature section of that original first chapter because of its research value, the material was cast into McAuleyana form and placed in Appendix A.

This work was completed through the joint contributions of much prayer, time, and effort on the part of many persons including my own religious sisters, and to all of these I am immeasurably indebted. Sincere appreciation is expressed, to mention but a few, to Sister M. Susanne Smith, S.S.M. of Saint Louis University, director of the thesis, for her sustaining encouragement especially in the early stages of development; to Sister Marie Jeanne d'Arc Hughes, R.S.M. of Detroit, Michigan, for lending her study on Mother M. Francis Bridgeman; to Sister M. Bertrand Degnan, R.S.M. and her religious Superiors of Albany, New York, for their generosity in making accessible source material that was available previously only in Ireland; and to Mother M. Dominick of the parenthouse in Ireland, for entrusting precious data to the cause.

Valued too are the reading of the thesis manuscript and the constructive recommendations of the Reverend John B. McGloin, S.J., Professor of History, University of San Francisco, prior to making plans for publication; the translation from the Spanish of Mercedarian source material by Dr. Carlos Sanchez, Ph.D., Assistant Professor of Spanish, University of San Francisco; and the liberality of the Consulate of Ireland situated in San Francisco and the Hospitals Commission in Dublin.

Not the least of the gratifying experiences are the friendships formed through correspondence with many Sisters of Mercy in various parts of the world and their genuine interest in the work.

Lastly, the writer has recourse to the language of silence while confiding to Mary her deep sentiments of gratitude to Mother M. Cyril and her assistants in Burlingame, California, for granting her the opportunity and the privilege to attempt an evaluation of the work of the Foundress, and in so doing to make better known Mother Mary Catherine McAuley's WAY OF MERCY in the care of the sick.

Sister Mary Beata

Feast of Corpus Christi
June 20, 1957

PART I

History Telescoped

Following the coming of St. Patrick in the fifth century and the spread of Christianity Ireland was titled the "Isle of Saints and Scholars." Monasteries were not only centers of learning but also preserved that learning for posterity by the copying of manuscripts. The famous Book of Kells, classed the most beautiful of the illuminated works in all the world, had a Celtic origin during the eighth century or a little earlier.[1] The contribution of the monasteries extended itself in a broad and varied usefulness.

Culture was the heritage of the Irish people. Gwynn[2] indicates that the four main elements of a culture comprise religious, political, economic, and social heritages. To these the Irish were to cling amid persecution, poverty, and a lack of educational opportunities. The political history of the British Crown and its effect on Ireland is inseparable from the story being recounted. An understanding of the mid-eighteenth to the mid-nineteenth century, the span within which Catherine McAuley lived (1778-1841), is essential as a backdrop against which to evaluate what she accomplished.

1. Social Changes

The ushering in of this period was not without achievement. Men could point with pride to the end of feudalism accomplished by their forefathers a century before and to

12

the transition into an industrial era in their own day. Older men, inclined to dwell on the past, could recall with joy the premiere in Dublin of Handel's oratorio, *The Messiah*, in 1742. Nevertheless, industry brought problems which turned the thoughtful to the present. It took the outspoken, caustic Jonathan Swift to awaken men to the specific problems being created, and in a special way to defend the Irish peasant.

Two movements were gaining momentum in England and in turn were affecting Ireland. The closing half of the eighteenth century found England engulfed in the human problems engendered by revolutionary changes, and looking to the nineteenth century for their solving. It was the age of a new civilization thriving on industrial power aggrandized by war. For over sixty years England was immersed in one war after another with only brief intervals between them.

The industrial revolution gave impetus to production which was now so essential. Coal mining and the smelting of iron reached a new high in output. For these reasons the utilization of child labor, under the severest of circumstances, was considered legitimate. Men like William Blake and later Charles Dickens used their pens to arouse the world to the plight of the children. From 1817 to 1819 attempts were made to pass laws which would prohibit children being used as "chimney sweeps."

"Apart from the dangers of suffocation in narrow or horizontal flues, the boys ran the risk of being burnt. . . . Most boys in the trade were stunted in growth, blear-eyed from the soot, and "knapped-kneed" from climbing when their bones were soft and from dragging heavy loads. . . . Some masters used to take them to the New River on Sunday mornings in the summer, but leave them coated with soot all winter."[3]

It is little wonder, then, that failure to pass these laws led to other bills, and that conditions gradually improved.

Men had become divided into classes, and the workers were divided further into the skilled and the unskilled. In the economic world voices were being heard for the "rights" and the welfare of the individual. Families concentrated in the industrial areas; the influx of people resulted in an unprecedented increase in population. Housing projects to provide adequate living quarters were not a part of early nineteenth-century government planning. Economics had brought wealth on the one hand and extreme poverty on the other.

"Unfortunately, the wealthier leaders of the Ascendancy had little sense of their civic responsibility towards the poverty-stricken masses that crowded together in the capital [Dublin]. . . . And, indeed, when help was forthcoming for the needs of the poor, too often it was to tempt them to barter away their one remaining possession—their faith."[4]

2. Religious Oppression

The choice to be made by Irish Catholics was between worldly prestige and riches and being a traitor to their conscience and their God. They chose poverty and their faith, which was priceless. The *Times*, six years after Mother McAuley's death, could still say with shame:

"In no other country has the wealth of the proprietor, the power of the magistrate and the accomplishments of the educated, been employed less for the benefit of the many, more for the gain and the pleasure of the few."[5]

This was a religious persecution which had been going on for two-and-a-half centuries. It was the same persecution which had brought the Puritans to America. Of Cromwell's dictatorship the historian has commented:

"Most bitter of all against the Cromwellian regime were

the Roman Catholics in Ireland. Though Cromwell as Lord Protector had favored tolerance for Protestants, it would be long before Catholics could forget the Irish priests whom Cromwell's soldiery had brutally knocked on the head, or the thousands of Catholic girls and boys whom Cromwell's agents had sold into horrible slavery in the West Indies."[6]

The next quarter of a century brought a brief respite only to be followed by the first of the new penal laws under William and Mary. The persecution of old was renewed and then intensified by succeeding rulers. John Morley has written pointedly:

"Let [men] turn candidly to the history of Ireland from 1691 down to 1798 and they will perceive that the diabolical prescription of the Penal Laws and the frenzied atrocities with which the Protestants suppressed the Catholic rising at the close of the century are absolutely unsurpassed in history."[7]

The practice of the Catholic religion in that long period of time was largely in hidden or out-of-the-way lanes and under cover of darkness.

England by now had entered upon her period of history when she was engaged in a political struggle with warring nations, and she was in need of the friendship and good will of her subordinate possessions. George III, ascending the throne in the midst of the Seven Years' War, had to face in turn the American War of Independence and later the Napoleonic Wars. These were important factors in instituting some relaxation in the penal code in 1782 under the Gardiner Act and in granting the Irish Parliament some legislative autonomy. That these concessions did not grant freedom of religion, however, will be evident in discussing the educational system of that period. There were still prices to be paid for retaining the faith. An eyewitness, the non-conformist English statesman, Edmund Burke, gives some insight into the degree of freedom that was actually attained. In reference to the Gardiner Act he wrote to a Peer of Ireland:

"It however still recites the oath, and that Catholics ought to be considered as good and loyal subjects to his majesty, his crown and government. Then follows an universal exclusion of those GOOD and LOYAL subjects, from every (even the lowest) office of trust and profit,—from any vote at any election,—from any privilege in a town corporate, from being even a freeman of such a corporation, —from serving on grand juries,—from a vote at a vestry,— from having a gun in his house,—from being a barrister, attorney, or solicitor, &c., &c., &c.

"This has surely much more the air of a table of prescription than an act of grace. What must we suppose the laws concerning those *good* subjects to have been, of which this is a relaxation."[8]

Thirteen years later, in 1795, when age had mellowed him perhaps and enriched his insight into human nature, Burke wrote to the Reverend Dr. Hussey of the Church of England:

"This religious persecution, like most others, has been carried on under the pretext of their being bad subjects, and disaffected to the government. I think it very possible that, to a degree, the ascendants were sincere. The understanding is soon debauched over to the passions; and our opinions very easily follow our wishes. When we are once ill-inclined to any man or set of men, we readily believe any evil of him or them that is inconvenient to our hostile designs."[9]

The year 1793 had brought the Catholic Relief Act but the Catholic Emancipation was not to be achieved until 1829 when Catherine McAuley was already well established in her life work. Names such as Manning and Newman, who were her contemporaries, and the movement begun at Oxford need but be mentioned to realize, too, that the Catholic Revival in England was bought at a great price.

3. Educational Barriers

The story of education in the Ireland under review parallels its persecution and poverty. One factor which must be kept in mind is the difference in attitude toward education which existed in the sister countries. It has been said that the children in England worked in the factories. The first Factory Act passed in England in 1802 provided that

"children were not to work more than twelve hours a day . . . part of the working day was to be given up to instruction in reading, writing and arithmetic . . . every Sunday they were to be instructed and examined in the principles of the Christian religion, by some proper person."[10]

Hannah Moore, Andrew Bell, and Joseph Lancaster were to attempt to improve the educational system. But the first vote regarding public money for education in England was to occur as late as two years after Mother McAuley founded her Congregation. This vote

"was denounced by Cobbett with great vehemence. His argument has been heard of, even a century later, so it is worth citing here. 'Education has been more and more spread. But what did it all tend to? Nothing, but to increase the number of schoolmasters and schoolmistresses—that new race of idlers. (Cobbett had clearly never spent half-a-day teaching a class!) Education has spread; crime, too, has increased.'

"This was the view of a democratic leader, at a time when some 45 per cent of the whole people of England could not write even their own names."[11]

That such a number was uneducated should not be shocking when it is recalled that England, together with European nations, was only approximately a century removed from feudalism.[12] There were universities and scholars in England as elsewhere but education was for the wealthy and the aristocratic classes.

In Ireland, in the century preceding Catherine McAuley's birth, steps had been taken to eliminate Catholic education not only in the homes and schools but also to make it impossible to receive that education abroad. For a period the struggle for education appeared hopeless but the desire, even on the part of the peasant, was soon rekindled. Visitors to Ireland from 1728 to 1828 were unanimous in recognizing this to be true. This may be due in part to the determination of Catholic Irish parents to teach their children the fundamentals of their faith despite opposition and penal laws. It gave rise to the misleadingly titled Hedge schools, where children, secluded from government officials and capable of quick dispersion, were taught under cover of the roadside hedge.

From 1782 to 1829 there was a supposed relaxation of the Gardiner Act but in reality the persecution assumed a more subtle form. Although Catholics were permitted to establish schools, these could not be endowed and it was necessary to obtain a license from the Protestant Bishop as well as for the teacher to take the Oath of Allegiance. Need it be added that what schools existed under these circumstances would be found only through close scrutiny. By the Catholic Relief Act of 1793 the stigma of the license clause for school recognition was removed.

For at least a half-century before this Dublin had convents of Dominican and Poor Clare nuns, where the daughters of the wealthy were taught. But Catholic wealth was a scarce commodity, and since no one desired to come face to face with the law in these early days, none of these schools had more than one hundred students enrolled at any one period.

In 1766 Teresa Mullaly began the first school in Dublin for the education of poor girls. Nine years later a kindred soul established a Sisterhood in Cork for the same purpose and the Foundress, Nano Nagle, wrote her friend in Dublin about her undertaking. Subsequently Teresa purchased and equipped George's Hill Convent in Dublin for which Nano Nagle promised to provide sisters. But she died in 1784 before achieving this goal. Eventually two young women were sent by Teresa to Cork to be trained as religious. In 1794, twenty-eight years after Teresa Mullaly had begun her work, she welcomed the return of these two religious to George's Hill.[13] This convent was to play an important role some thirty-six years later in the religious formation of Catherine McAuley.

PART II

A DESTINY FASHIONED

BAGGOT STREET, Coolock House, Stormanstown are names enshrined in the heart of every Sister of Mercy because they are links in the life of their Foundress, Mother Mary Catherine McAuley, and serve as guides in reviewing the story of her life.

1. *Early Life at Stormanstown and in Dublin*

It was at Stormanstown, on the outskirts of Dublin, that Catherine McAuley was born on Michaelmas day, September 29. The exact year has been disputed and is given by various biographers as 1778, 1781, and 1787. Savage was the first one who used the year 1781, giving reasons for his choice. The year 1787 appears on Mother McAuley's tombstone and as such has been transmitted in a number of her biographies including those by Hartnett and Carroll. It corresponds with an entry in the register at George's Hill concerning Catherine's reception of the religious habit "on the 9th December, 1830 being 44 years of age."[1] By these numbers she would have passed her forty-third birthday two months previously. A record of James Mc(G)auley's will is carried in Sir William Betham's *Genealogical Abstracts* although the will itself has perished probably in the destruction of the Four Courts in 1916. The will was probated in August, 1783.[2] On this basis it is now definitely established that 1787 for Catherine's birth was an error. It could well have been the result of an early error in transposing the last two numbers. Murphy used the year 1778 in the first extensive sketch of Catherine's life written in 1847. That year was accepted for the purpose of this study.

No record of Catherine's baptism exists. Those of the parish in which Stormanstown was situated are incomplete. Of baptisms during the years of persecution it has been written:

"Before the date of Catholic Emancipation in Ireland i.e. 1829, I understand Baptisms were conferred in private houses and the number of parishes in which records go back to the beginning of the last century are very few."[3]

Catherine's was a happy childhood spent in close association with a father whose Catholic faith found expression in the spiritual and corporal works of mercy. While James McAuley was considerably older than his wife, Elinor, both lived in a period of religious persecution. Because of the difference in age it is possible that James McAuley had become more acutely aware of the bitterness of that persecution, and of the poverty to which it led. Historians are in accord in attributing to the marriage a combination of sincere Catholicity and Christian charity on the part of the husband with the talent and natural virtue on the part of the wife. These were to be blended in their daughter, Catherine, and were to characterize her life—God's grace to love His poor supernaturalizing the charm which marked her as a lady.

Early in the political period of the so-called relaxation of the penal code, James McAuley died leaving his widow with two young daughters, Catherine and Mary, and an infant son, James. Elinor McAuley found it necessary to sell Stormanstown and to preside over a smaller home in Dublin. This home she also sold in three years and went to live with her friend, a Mrs. St. George, at a time when

"Dublin Protestants enjoyed [a] sense of superiority even more than their English brethren; their fewness in comparison to the overwhelming majority of the Catholic Irish gave them the exclusiveness of a ruling caste."[4]

For the remaining twelve years of Mrs. McAuley's life she was to expose herself and her three young children to an atmosphere of "constant intercourse with persons whose conversation was calculated to weaken the spirit of Catholicity in their minds."[5] Illness may have prevented her from assuming full responsibility for the children's reception of the sacraments but it is known that

"Catherine received her first Holy Communion from the hand of Dr. Murray, the future Archbishop of Dublin, in the parish church of St. Paul's, Arran Quay, and was confirmed there by Archbishop Troy. . . . It is very probable that it was in [the] year, 1796, that he confirmed Catherine."[6]

Mary and James, however, were to succumb to the example of the mother in the indifference to things Catholic by which they were surrounded. Remorsefully, the dying Elinor McAuley was harassed with the thought when there was little she could do to rectify the situation. On tradition it is believed that the priest was brought to her bedside before her death in 1798. This deathbed scene was to leave a lasting impression on Catherine. Her own fear until almost the last moments of her life of appearing before a just God, and her devotedness in bringing God's mercy to the dying may be traced, undoubtedly, to this sad experience in her young womanhood.

The three orphans were now to be separated. The two younger children were taken by a distant maternal relative and his wife, Mr. and Mrs. William Armstrong, who were both staunch Protestants. Catherine was to share the home of Mrs. McAuley's brother, Dr. Owen Conway, a surgeon,

Stormanstown House
Birthplace of Catherine McAuley

Return of the Sisters of Mercy to Coolock House
1955

Coolock House
Home of the Callaghans and of Miss McAuley

The House on Baggot Street
Later named St. Catherine's Convent

Present Parenthouse of Sisters of Mercy
Carysfort Park, Blackrock, Co. Dublin

and his daughter. For a short while Catherine knew again what it meant to be surrounded by Catholics and to enjoy the companionship of her young cousin, Ann. Through Ann Conway she met a priest who, in God's providence, was to counsel her on some future occasions.

Within a year Dr. Conway's "stock market" crashed and the family group was faced with absolute poverty. Catherine gained her first personal experience of being truly poor. As a gesture in relieving the Conway situation, Mr. Armstrong invited Catherine to join her sister and brother. In this home for about three years Catherine McAuley again heard the dogmas of her faith assailed and saw its adherents looked upon with scorn. But God was to send her aid. A neighbor and druggist confrere of Mr. Armstrong, Mr. William Callaghan and his wife, were frequent visitors. This older couple with no children of their own were instrumental in changing Catherine's future. Mr. Callaghan, who was planning to retire and buy a house in the country, asked Catherine to share their home and be a companion to his wife.

2. Life at Coolock House

In the autumn of 1803, several months after Catherine joined them, the Callaghans moved to Coolock House, a Georgian home situated on a twenty-two acre estate about three miles from Dublin. An added nineteen years of Catherine's life were spent in an environment that was not Catholic, where Catholicism was not approved, and where external evidence of it was not tolerated. Her early biographer wrote:

"Though invariably kind to her, she was aware that in matters of religion they were uncompromising.

"They amply supplied her with all she cared to use of this world's goods, and took pleasure in witnessing her alms-giving and the sweetness which enhanced the value of whatever she did to relieve the distressed. She had a special talent for comforting the suffering and the sorrowful, and thus no one ever applied to her for solace that did not experience the soothing influence of her pious words, while her zeal made her a missionary to the needy for miles around."[7]

Catherine was not restricted from going to Mass when she could; the limits imposed upon her were in bringing religion into the home. The innate kindness of the Callaghans provided the scope for her charitable designs, and what they recognized as philanthropy was for their all-but-adopted daughter the fulfilling of the second commandment. By her example and silent prayer she was to win for both of them eventually the gift of baptism.

Close contact with her for more than sixteen years brought home to the aging couple that Catherine's religion was the source of her unselfishness.

Mr. Callaghan outlived his wife by three years. These he spent scrutinizing yet more closely Catherine's work among the poor of the neighborhood. She had much more time now to call her own than when she had nursed his invalid wife. Though the circumstances differed he found the spirit which animated her not unlike that which she had manifested in caring for Mrs. Callaghan in her last illness. To these last two years of noble devotedness to his wife he had but to add the earlier fourteen years of unwavering graciousness. The extra time that Catherine had at her disposal was spent again, not on herself, but on others. His conviction grew that she was worthy of his trust. At his death in November, 1822, his will revealed that he had named her, ten months earlier, the sole possessor of his estate. After bequeathing small amounts in stocks and bonds to a number of individuals, he placed a codicil to his will which read:

"I do . . . hereby nominate, constitute and appoint the

said Catherine McAuley sole residuary legatee of all my estate and effects real or personal subject to the specific legacies mentioned in my will."[8]

The Standard[9] of October 7, 1955, carrying the story of the Sisters of Mercy's purchase and return to Coolock House, listed the value of the estate at Mr. Callaghan's death as 25,000 pounds; several months later *The Irish Independent*[10] translated that sum into present-day values as 250,000 pounds. In American money that would be $700,000.

The recipient of this bounty made no immediate or drastic changes in her manner of living. From Coolock House she continued ministering to the needs of the poor of the vicinity. "She now devised a regular system of distributing food and clothing . . . these were daily dispensed to the needy."[11] Gradually the realm of her activity widened. At the request of Father Nugent, who knew her well, she began to teach the children in his parish and to provide for their wants.

"Always a believer in teaching people to help themselves rather than encourage them to be content with charity, Catherine set to work to teach the girls needlework, knitting, and other home crafts. . . . Catherine next decided to rent the house next door to the Poor School, and in it opened a Repository where she exhibited and sold her pupils' work to her wealthy friends. With the proceeds the girls were able to purchase material to make up for their own use, or provide some of their other needs."[12]

This work of charity opened up greater horizons. Catherine saw the need for a place of her own which would serve as a school and as a shelter for women without a home. For Catherine to recognize a need was to seek counsel and to act. Through Father Nugent she had met Father Armstrong. He and his friend, Father Blake, were to be her guides in

her decision. Within two years after her benefactor's death
the cornerstone had been laid for the building she hoped
to erect. "The first stone . . . was blessed and laid by Dr.
Blake, Vicar General of the Diocese, and afterwards Bishop
of Dromore, in July, 1824."[13] Three years later the building
was completed.

3. Life at the House on Baggot Street

The House on Baggot Street opened a new period in
Catherine McAuley's life—the remainder of her life. Within
a year she had broken all ties with Coolock House by selling
it together with all its furnishings, keeping only what was
practical in her work in her new home. She had closed the
door to the past; she opened it upon a future to be spent
with and for Christ's poor.

The architect had received instructions to construct a
house with some large rooms suitable for classrooms and
dormitories, with one room of greater height for a chapel,
and some smaller rooms to accommodate those who might
wish to join Catherine in her work. She anticipated doing a
small work for God with the cooperation of a few women
with similar ideals of dedication. She could not foresee that
after one-hundred-twenty-seven years these few women
would increase to almost 25,000 and would buy back
Coolock House in testimony of her memory; to walk again
literally in her footsteps as well as in her spirit.

The works of mercy at Baggot Street began on the Feast
of Our Lady of Mercy, September 24, 1827. School was
taught that day and some women were given shelter. On
the first Christmas the custom was established of providing
a Christmas dinner for poor children and of distributing
supplies to poor families. Within the next year plans were
made to assume greater responsibilities. Catherine wrote:

"With full approbation of His Grace the Archbishop the

Institution in Baggot Street is to go according to the original intention. Ladies who prefer a Conventual life and are prevented embracing it from the nature of property or connections may retire to this House. It is expected a gratuity will be given and an annual pension paid sufficient to meet the expenses a lady must incur. The objects which the Charity at present embrace are daily education of hundreds of poor female children and instruction of young women who sleep in the House.

"Objects in view—superintendence of young women employed in the House, instructing and assisting the sick poor as may hereafter be approved."[14]

On the first anniversary of the opening of the house, September 24, 1828, word was received from Dr. Murray, the Archbishop, that the institution could be dedicated to the Mother of God under her title of Mercy. From that day it became known as the House of Mercy. When Dr. Murray called on the Feast of St. Cecilia he granted the group of workers, who playfully styled one another sister, the privilege "to assume a distinctive religious dress and visit the sick, both in private houses and in public hospitals."[15]

Mother Aikenhead's Sisters of Charity, founded in Dublin in 1815, were also visiting the sick in their homes. But neither 1815 nor 1828 provided a warrant by law for religious foundations. Catherine McAuley and her small band of helpers pioneered a work when "it was not permitted at this time for the members of any religious body in Dublin to visit these hospitals."[16] The day chosen to begin these visitations was the Feast of St. Andrew, the patron of the parish, November 30, 1828. How this was accomplished despite the bigotry of the age is a story in itself which will be alluded to again when developing this objective of her Institute.

It was either her good work or Catherine herself that attracted followers. It has been written:

"She was a sort of Pied Piper of Hamelin. They gathered to her, they foregathered with her; they went to live with her in the big new barrack; they left off their fine clothes and put on a plain dress; they said prayers with zealous exactitude at fixed hours; but they made no vows."[17]

That the group did not take vows but patterned their lives, nevertheless, on that of religious was to bring a certain censure on the House of Mercy. In the midst of this trial Catherine McAuley lost her trusted guide, the Reverend Dr. Armstrong. His parting message to her: "Do not put your trust in any human being; place all your confidence in God alone,"[18] was to be her strength in the face of misunderstanding. Her reaction to an opponent who assumed responsibility to inform her that the Archbishop was considering turning over her undertaking to Mother Aikenhead's community denotes her humility and its corollary, trust in God.

"She raised her heart to God, and in that moment sacrificed all to Him—the realization of her hopes and charitable projects from her early years, the zealous companions of her pious labors, the establishment on which she had expended her fortune—all; and meekly, serenely turning to her visitor, replied that she would acquiesce in the Archbishop's decision."[19]

In this trial Dr. Blake was Catherine McAuley's constant advocate. His own love of the poor made him appreciate what she was trying to do. He himself was attempting to match her work with girls by a similar one for boys. He founded the first of Dublin's Boys' Clubs made up of his fond little chimney sweeps, and his Christmas dinner was taken in their midst. At the beginning of Catherine's work he had said:

"I look upon Miss McAuley as one selected by Heaven for some great work. Her heart overflows with the charity of Jesus, whose all-consuming love burns within her. No woman has ever accomplished more for suffering, sorrowful humanity."[20]

God, however, did not demand of her the sacrifice of the work; what He did require was the submission of her will to His in the manner in which the work was to be accomplished. It was true that the objectives of the group who lived together at Baggot Street had been clearly defined, they wore a simple dress, assembled for common prayer and spiritual reading, and devoted time to private prayer and assistance at Holy Mass. They resembled and followed many of the practices of religious. There were those who thought that even the large, plain building looked like a convent. Yet these things of themselves do not make a religious and there was nothing further from Catherine's intention than that they be such.

But the spiritual edifice that she was destined to erect in the Church had the Divine Architect for designer. In God's plan, she was to be the instrument by which His mercy would be channeled and then diffused to the souls for whom His Divine Son had died upon a Cross. So it was that Catherine McAuley, a mature woman in love with Christ's poor and docile to His inspirations, would learn to walk in paths not of her choosing. God had not revealed His plans fully to her at the beginning but worked through her to execute His ends. Now He would go a step further. He would encircle her love for the poor in a union of her heart with His. To gain His complete love He asked for the renunciation of a will that was averse to being a religious and to trust herself fully to Him. Was she revealing her sentiments of this period of her life when, later, she was to say to her novices:

"In desiring His disciples to repose, Our Blessed Saviour called them not to entire separation from creatures but to a more intimate union of heart with God. It is an invitation He gives us also that we may serve Him with great confidence, free from a slavish fear unworthy of a child of God and a Spouse of Jesus Christ."[21]

His grace triumphed in her soul. Catherine McAuley, who might have lived a short while doing a certain amount of good and then have passed into oblivion as far as men were concerned, became instead the Foundress of the second largest religious congregation of women in the Catholic Church.[22]

4. A New Religious Congregation

God's desire that the group at Baggot Street continue the work as religious was made known to them by Dr. Murray, the Archbishop of Dublin. Catherine discussed the matter with her companions and conveyed their decision to His Excellency. The Feast of Our Lady's Nativity in 1830 became a memorable one. On that day Catherine McAuley exchanged her role of authority for that of a beginner to be instructed by others. She and two of her associates crossed the streets of Dublin that September eighth to present themselves at the Presentation Convent, George's Hill. Nine others remained at Baggot Street to carry on the work in their absence. Catherine McAuley, Anna Maria Doyle, and Elizabeth Harley went to the Presentation Sisters to learn the nature of the religious life and the obligations assumed in pronouncing the vows of religion. Those chosen to instruct the neophytes were charged with the grave responsibility of ascertaining their intention to strive for perfection —the primary end of all religious life.

The future Foundress was not to be spared. What would have been impossible to unaided human nature was attainable because of a reciprocal love. Certainly she could speak from experience when writing later to a young woman who was anticipating entering her congregation:

"It is a great triumph over nature. The grace must flow from Our Divine Redeemer Who came on earth not to bring the delusive enjoyment which we call peace but a heavenly sword sharpened on the cross to cut those dearest ties that have such strong hold on the heart and thus to draw all to Himself."[23]

At last the longed-for goal was reached. Catherine and her two companions pronounced their vows of poverty, chastity, and obedience. It *was* December 12, 1831; it *is* foundation day for the Sisters of Mercy.

Those at Baggot Street were awaiting with eager hearts the return of the trio. Bidding a fond and grateful farewell to the Presentation Sisters, the three immediately returned to share with their associates their new-found joy. There was no prevision vouchsafed Catherine that day, that before the deeds of a decade of years were to slip between her fingers, they would be still in death.

Yet in that short span Mother Mary Catherine McAuley anchored her religious institute upon the mercy of God. In that mercy, chastened by the Cross of Christ and ennobled by His Mother's intercession, the congregation she founded multiplied a thousandfold.

She lived to see it take root, and during the years 1836 to 1841 saw it spread in Ireland and to Great Britain. Interest in the foundations brought a request for information regarding the qualifications for a Sister of Mercy. In 1836 she gave the following reply:

"In compliance with your desire, Reverend Sir, I shall submit what seems 'generally' requisite for a Sister of Mercy.

"Besides an ardent desire to be united to God and serve the poor she must feel a particular interest for the sick and the dying; otherwise, the duty of visiting them would soon become exceedingly toilsome. She should be healthy, have

a feeling, distinct, impressive manner of speaking and reading—a mild countenance expressive of sympathy and patience, and there is so much to be required as to reserve and
recollection passing through the public ways—caution and
prudence on the visits—that it is desirable she begin rather
young, before habits and manners are so long formed as not
to be likely to alter.

"I beg again to remark that this is what seems generally
necessary. I am aware exceptions may be met and that
when there is a decided preference for the Order and other
essential dispositions conformity in practice might be accomplished at any period in life."[24]

Mother McAuley accompanied the sisters to each new
foundation and remained until the house was well established. Ordinarily, she would include a novice or postulant,
and provide for a ceremony of reception of the holy habit or
the profession of vows before her return to Baggot Street
as a means of arousing interest on the part of the people.
She maintained correspondence with the sisters on the foundations and in this way helped to cement the spirit of the
new and growing congregation. Catholic Emancipation was
too recent to address the sisters publicly by their religious
title. The envelopes of her letters bear the title Mrs. Warde
or Moore or Purcell, for example, while the salutations iden-
tify the sister as she was named in religion. In the account
of Mother McAuley written by Reverend Dominic Murphy
in 1847 he referred to her as Mrs. McAuley. This was the
common practice for religious of the penal and early post-
penal days. Walsh spoke for the appropriateness of the practice in this way:

"Mrs. is an abbreviation of mistress, which is the femi-
nine correlative of master. It was formerly a title of address
or courtesy nearly equivalent to madam, applied to any
woman or girl, but now chiefly and specifically to married

women. During the Elizabethan and Jacobean times and even in Queen Anne's day a woman who had mastered any art or branch of study was called a mistress and the original meaning of the word was a woman with authority or power of control, as over a house or over other persons, a female head, chief or director. The assumption of this title, now reserved only for the married, was perfectly in accord with the usage of the time."[25]

Mother McAuley's letters give an insight into her human qualities and reveal her ability to blend the everyday occurrences of life with spiritual realities so symbolic of the unity of her whole life. Two letters written on December 20, 1840 testify to this and the one has particular interest today when the square dance has regained popularity. The first was written to a young religious:

"My dearest Sister M. deSales,
. . . I think sometimes our passage through this dear sweet world is something like the dance called *Right and Left*. You and I have crossed over, changed places, &.&. Your set is finished—for a little time you'll dance no more but I have now to go through the figure called *Sir Roger de Coverly*—too old perhaps for your memory [26]. I'll have to curtsey and bow in Birr presently, to change corners going from the one I am in at present to another, take hands of everyone who does me the honor, and end the figure by coming back to my own place. I'll then have a seasaw dance to Liverpool and a merry jig that has no stop to Birmingham —and I hope a second to Bermondsey where you, Sister M. Xavier, and I will join hands and dance the 'Duval Trio' back on the same ground. We have one solid comfort— amidst this little tripping about—our hearts can always be in the same place, centered in God, for Whom alone we go forward or stay back. Oh, may He look on us with love and pity, and then we shall be able to do anything He wishes

us to do no matter how difficult to accomplish or painful to our feelings. If He looks on us with approbation for one instant each day it will be sufficient to bring us joyfully on to the end of our journey. Let us implore Him to do so at this season of Love and Mercy."

Then as she wrote to a superior, Mrs. Moore in Limerick, or Sister Mary Elizabeth, she commented on the above letter by saying:

"As I must go through the rounds of writing called 'The Foundation Circulars' after having finished to Mother Clare in England and Sister Xavier I really did not know what to say to my poor Sister M. deSales from whom I have two or three unanswered letters, when some lively spirit suggested the thought of dancing through it."

And after quoting the letter with slight alterations she continued:

"Now what shall I say to yourself? Worn out as I am— you don't require much—your path is now 'strewed with flowers' for the bazaar and all the pretty dolls and toys will bring you back to the gaiety of your childhood, and when you see them change into bread and broth and blankets [for the poor] your heart will rejoice and your offering will —I trust—be rendered fully acceptable by the pure love which produces it. May God grant you every blessing—I will write to you from Birr—Pray often for your ever affectionate
                                                        M. C. McAuley"

The first convent built in England since the Reformation had the illustrious Pugin for architect. It was located in Bermondsey near London and was offered to Mother McAuley if she would send a foundation of sisters. Two young sisters had been sent from England to Ireland to

Mother of Mercy

Adapted from a miraculous painting (1587) in the church of St. Pudenziana in Rome. In 1890, Pope Leo XIII designated this as the emblem of the Sisters of Mercy.

make their novitiate. In 1839 they returned with Mother M. Clare as superior. A member of the first group professed at Baggot Street, Mother Clare would later, in 1854, accompany Florence Nightingale to the Crimea.

No time was lost by Mother McAuley to hold a reception at Bermondsey which happened to be the first public religious ceremony held in centuries. "No sacred function at all approaching it in splendor had been seen in Great Britain since the pre-Reformation times."[27] Mother McAuley was present on this occasion when an earl's daughter received the habit. Two years later she wrote:

"Just got a letter from England—their ceremony over, four professed and one received—Lady Barbara fixed at last a humble Sister of Mercy, the first titled lady to become a nun in England or Ireland for a long time. There have been Honorables but not an earl's daughter for centuries."[28]

Three months later she wrote another letter which indicates the cosmopolitan nature which her community was assuming:

"I am quite renovated by a delightful addition to the flock. On Wednesday last the first Scotch Sister that has joined an Irish community. Sister Cecilia became acquainted with Mrs. (Captain) Osbourne, a Scotch lady who goes every year to see her friends in Edinburgh and through her this sweet Sister came—twenty-two years old, most interesting. The variety of accents is now quite amusing at recreation. She was never out of Scotland before."[29]

The new community continued to spread. Requests for sisters came from Scotland and Newfoundland. But the Foundress' life was drawing to a close. In words written on her last Mercy Day spent on this earth she gave the secret of her success: "We have ever confided largely in Divine

Providence and shall continue to do so."[30] One of her last joys was to receive papal approbation of the Rule for the Sisters of Mercy.

Mother McAuley's death on November 11, 1841, occurred less than ten years after her profession. The account in the daily paper read:

DEATH OF MRS. CATHERINE McAULEY OF THE HOUSE OF MERCY

"This truly pious and patriotic Irish woman should not drop into the tomb like those who leave no trace of usefulness behind them. With a mind, a person, and an independent fortune which might command exalted rank in any point of Christendom, she piously embraced the Cross, and practiced as far as any mortal could, her Savior's noblest attribute.

"The House of Mercy in Baggot Street and fourteen similar establishments in various parts of the Empire, namely those of Kingstown, Booterstown, Tullamore, Carlow, Naas, Galway, Limerick, Wexford, Charleville, Cork, Parsonstown (Birr), Bermondsey, Liverpool, and Birmingham were her own foundations, and after seeing about one hundred spiritual daughters walking in her path she expired . . . of a disease which she contracted in the discharge of what she deemed her duty."[31]

But for the true Sister of Mercy Mother McAuley still lives. She lives also in the words of those who are not her spiritual children. Two years ago this was written:

"In a deep peace she breathed her last on the evening of November 11, 1841. It was not the end of her labour. Over the years her daughters have been bringing her message of mercy to a world of suffering and need. And over the years God has been revealing that from beyond the grave Catherine McAuley is the unchanging mother still. Baggot

Street may claim her body. But the Church claims her heart."[32]

Yes, her legacy to the Church and mankind lives in the message of mercy transmitted by those whom she herself styled her "Children in Christ!"[33] This is her monument established on earth—yet reaching to heaven.

PART III

A Way of Mercy

CATHERINE McAULEY, true daughter of the Church within which she established her religious congregation, found the inspiration for her particular work in God and His Church. To this she joined the best which science had to offer in the care of the sick. She formulated principles without naming them or perhaps recognizing them as scientific and practiced the art of nursing in a spirit of mercy.

1. Dedication to Our Lady of Mercy

The mercy of Christ is channeled to men through Mary. It is no wonder, then, that in choosing to devote her life to the salvation of souls, Catherine McAuley was drawn to our Blessed Mother under this title.

She recalled an old religious order in the Church founded at the command of Our Lady herself. On the night of August 1, 1218, Mary had requested that a religious order be established to free the Christian slaves who were suffering at the hands of the Moors on the Iberian peninsula. On that occasion three distinct apparitions were made to three different persons: to Peter Nolasco, whose life at court was distinguished by his compassion for the poor; to Raymond of Pennafort, his confessor; and to James I, King of Aragon, friend of Peter and counselee of Raymond.

Peter, of the noble and wealthy family of Nolasco, was born in France about 1189. At the death of his father when

Peter was fifteen he became heir to the estate. Later he consecrated himself to God by vow, distributed his wealth to the poor, and journeyed to Spain the greater part of which was under control of the infidels.

At Barcelona, Peter Nolasco spent his substance in redeeming those whose faith and virtue were exposed to spiritual dangers under their Mohammedan masters. He encouraged others to help him not only by contributing alms but also by joining him in the work. When his designs were opposed, the Mother of Mercy intervened by appealing to three on whom she could rely.

"Here were three, a King, a Canon, and a cavalier, chosen by God and His Blessed Mother . . . to found an order. . . . Nor were they found wanting or negligent of the charge committed to them, for on the 10th day of August, 1218, in the Cathedral Church of St. Eulalia, in Barcelona, the Order of Ransom or Mercy was formally founded.

"From the hands of the Most Reverend Bishop, Don Berenguer de Palou, Peter Nolasco and twelve others, his first companions, received the white woolen habit of the Order, tunic, scapular and cowl. To this vesture, symbolic of the purity of Our Lady, James I added the arms or shield of his kingdom, the red and gold bars of the ancient coat of Aragon. And the Canons of the Cathedral Chapter, not to be outdone, gave the white cross of St. Eulalia on a red field. To this day this shield is worn by the religious of the Order of Ransom or Mercy, the white cross signifying the Christian faith and purity of life and motive, the bars of Aragon emblematic of willing sacrifice and of blood to be shed in actual or equivalent martyrdom. For to the three vows of religion—Poverty, Chastity, and Obedience—they add a fourth, these heroes of Christian charity, to offer themselves as hostages for the redemption of Christian captives."[1]

Burton, without documenting her source, sketched a ro-

mantic origin for the red bars in the Aragon coat of arms. An
ancestor of the king by the name of Geoffrey, wounded in
battle, was asked by his emperor how he wished his valor
to be rewarded. Upon being requested for an emblem for
Geoffrey's unblazened shield, the emperor "dipped his hand
in the blood flowing from the knight's wound, and drew a
pattern on the white ground of the shield."[2] The shield still
used by the Order of Ransom or Mercy has five gold bars
and four red ones.

It may have been the two-tone bars of this shield
which prompted Mother McAuley to attach a symbolism
to the numbers by saying: "Mercy has five letters corresponding to the five Sacred Wounds of our Sweet Savior; it
begins with M and ends with Y, like the name of His ever
Blessed Mother."[3] This shield is used by the Sisters of Mercy
as their insignia, and is incorporated into the graduate nurse
pins of many of their schools of nursing. Some have retained
the red bars and background; others have substituted blue
to symbolize our Blessed Mother. The five-ranked gold bars
idealize our Savior's mercy.

Another link with the ancient Mercedarian Order may
be Mother McAuley's choice of a white mantle to be worn
in the chapel by her sisters on certain feast days and for
certain functions. Certainly the shield-like guimpe, helmet-
like coif, and the white cross on a field of black, incorporated by the Foundress into the religious habit, point to the
influence of these Knights of Mercy.

The part which Our Blessed Mother under her title of
Mercy has played in the New World where more than half
of the Sisters of Mercy labor is of particular significance.

Most historians record the fact that the motley crew
which accompanied Columbus on his eventful trip in 1492
watched the setting of the sun during their many days
aboard ship while they sang their evening hymn of praise
to the Mother of God: "Hail Holy Queen, Mother of Mercy."
For the most part, however, they fail to mention that Colum-

bus took with him on this journey a priest and that the priest belonged to the Order of Mercy. Yet in the *Annals* of the Order published in Barcelona in 1669 this summary was given:

"The world is indebted to this signal man [the Provincial Fray George of Seville] for a great part of the benefit which all of it received with the discovery of the West Indies; for having helped Christopher Columbus, patronizing his intentions, supporting his arguments and giving him food and shelter in which to live for many months in the convent of LA MERCED DE CORDOVA. There he solved many and important needs which he had; until the noteworthy foundation of his proposition was understood and he was sent upon his way with the blessing of the Catholic Queen Isabel. In gratitude for so many benefits, the Admiral took with him as chaplain Fray Juan Infante, son of the city and the convent of Xerez de La Frontera, and then the Vicar of the aforesaid convent of Cordova, in the first fleet that left Spain in order to discover these new lands. This man was the first priest who is known to have seen the New World since the apostle St. Thomas. He was also the first who celebrated the holy sacrifice of the Mass there and who preached the holy gospel. . . . There is a firm tradition in all those parts concerning this truth. . . . There are authentic testimonials about everything in the Royal Council of the Indies; and in conformity with these and the daily records that Admiral Christopher Columbus remitted about what happened on his first discoveries the chronicler Pedro Martyr de Angleria . . . wrote with all legality. . . . In the first cloister of the convent DE LA MERCED DE XEREZ DE LA FRONTERA there has been for a long time in this place the statue of the same Fray Juan Infante . . . and at its feet, the Latin inscription: . . . Accompanying Christopher Columbus in the discovery of the Islands of the Indies. . . . There he said the first Mass; and in order to take possession of

America in the name of Jesus Christ Crucified, he turned around the Consecrated Host in his hands and exhibited it to the four corners of the earth."[4]

Well can authors indicate casually that the Admiral Columbus summoned on his second voyage "all hands to prayer on the quarter-deck, where they sing the *Salve* and other prayers and hynms very devoutly, rendering thanks to our Lord."[5] Long before on his first voyage a priest had offered thanks to God and honored Christ's Mother under the title of Our Lady of Mercy. In identifying the priest of this trip a member of the Order provided the following explanation to the writer:

"There are many reasons why it had to be our Order. Our Order was the royal Order of Spain and as such had the duty of providing chaplains for the army and for the navy of Spain. Our Order was from the very beginning the only Order which had its own ships to sail to Africa, Minor Asia, and the Balkan States after they had been occupied by the Mohammedans. Sailing was a very important part of the [work of the] members of the Order."[6]

The Mercy Annalist could testify in 1669:

"Since the first Armada of Columbus left for the discovery of the Indies, or the New World, not one until this day has left Spain for those parts without taking religious of the Order of Mercy in order to follow up the spiritual conquest that Fray Juan Infante began with such prosperous aspects."[7]

Historians describing the conquest of Mexico tell of the practice of the priests of the Order of Mercy setting up altars in the pagan temples of the conquered lands. Cortez, in the first land occupied by him on a small island off the coast of Mexico, gave orders to clean the pagan temples of the sacrificial blood of the idols. His chaplain and counselor, Father Bartholomew De Olmedo, erected the first Christian altar with a cross and the picture of the Blessed Mother. This same priest sent to Emperor Montezuma in Mexico City an image of Our Lady before the Spaniards reached the city. In 1528 Cortez had overthrown the Aztec dynasty.

"A procession of the whole army was then formed with Father Olmedo at its head. The soiled and tattered banners of Castile, which had waved over many a field of battle, now threw their shadows on the peaceful array of the soldiery, as they slowly moved along, rehearsing the litany, and displaying the image of the Virgin and the blessed symbol of man's redemption. The revered father pronounced a discourse, in which he briefly reminded the troops of their great cause for thankfulness to Providence for conducting them safe through their long and perilous pilgrimage; and dwelling on the responsibility incurred by their present position, he besought them not to abuse the rights of conquest, but to treat the unfortunate Indians with humanity. The sacrament was then administered to the commander-in-chief and the principal cavaliers and the services concluded with a solemn thanksgiving to the God of battles, who had enabled them to carry the banner of the Cross triumphant over this barbaric empire."[8]

Three years later Our Lady appeared to the Indian peasant, Juan Diego, on the Mexican summit of Tepeyac, to assure him that she was a compassionate Mother.

"Know and take heed, thou, the least of my sons, that I am Holy Mary, ever Virgin Mother of the True God for whom we live, the Creator of all the world, Maker of Heaven and Earth. I urgently desire that a temple should be built to me here, to bear witness to my love, my compassion, my succor and protection. For I am a merciful Mother to thee and to all thy fellow people on this earth

who love me and trust me and invoke my help. I listen to
their lamentations and solace all their sorrows and their
sufferings."[9]

Mary appeared to Juan Diego four times in the space of
three days with the last apparition occurring on December
12, 1531.

Three centuries passed. On December 12, 1831, Mother
Mary Catherine McAuley founded the Sisters of Mercy to
extend the work of this merciful Mother. She adapted the
work of Peter Nolasco to the needs of her age and her
people, and because these needs belonged to mankind the
means she used would endure.

2. *The Mercy Rule and Constitution*

Three years before Mother McAuley had pronounced
her vows, she outlined the visitation and care of the sick
as one of the particular works of the group assembled at
Baggot Street. When she wrote the Constitutions which were
to govern her community this was to be the one notable
difference from those that served her as models.

Once her decision had been made to establish the House
of Mercy as a religious institute she studied a number of
holy rules of the convents in and near Dublin. The Carmel-
ites and Poor Clares both offered to affiliate the house to
their own but how this would have been accomplished is
not clear. But Catherine herself recognized that the rules of
these contemplative orders did not coincide with the work
she anticipated. That of the Presentation Sisters was the
ultimate choice. Their rule was based on that of the Ursulines; and the Ursuline rule, in turn, on the Augustinian rule.

Near the close of the fourth century St. Augustine and
a few companions began to lead a monastic life at Tagaste;
from here Augustine later was called to become the Bishop
of Hippo. Since he popularized monasticism in Africa he is

considered its founder in that country. No certainty exists, however, that his monks followed a special rule.

A monastery of nuns also was founded by Augustine. His sister presided over this monastery in the episcopal city until her death. A letter from Augustine to these nuns contains what generally is referred to as his rule.

"That which bears the name of St. Augustine is taken from a letter addressed by the Holy Doctor to nuns in the year 423. It was afterwards accommodated to the use of men, but when and under what circumstances this was done is not certain. Both the Canons Regular and the Hermits of St. Augustine endeavor to trace their descent from the monks established by St. Augustine, but the subject still remains a subject of controversy."[10]

In 1256 many religious groups of the Order of Hermits which had been following the above rule united under one superior.

The rule of St. Augustine for nuns consists of eleven short chapters dealing with general matters. No reference is made to any particular work in which the sisters might engage, such as education or the care of the sick. Chapter I covering the End and Spirit of the Institute reads: "First, my dear Sisters, love God above all things, and secondly, your neighbor as yourselves; for those two commandments have been given to us principally."[11]

This rule served as the basis for that of many religious congregations for women. But before Mother McAuley patterned the Constitutions for her Institute on any of them, papal decrees were issued which affected all religious orders.

Since the pontificate of Innocent III the bishops no longer had the power to approve religious communities in their diocese. Succeeding popes, and in particular Boniface VIII, imposed yet more constricting regulations for religious women requiring of all solemn vows and the cloister. The

Council of Trent (1545-63) confirmed the decrees of Boniface VIII.

To Pius V, ascending the pontifical throne two years after the close of the Council, fell the responsibility of carrying forward the directives imposed by the Council of Trent. In his first year as pope, Pius V issued the constitution, *Circa Pastoralis.* His interpretation of earlier decrees was that unless solemn vows were taken and the strict cloister was imposed the Order was denied the privilege of accepting new members. This explains the enclosure common to the orders founded in this period. Except for the fact that this constitution met only with partial observance it would have meant the gradual extinction of sisters with simple vows.

"For a long time the succeeding Popes sought to apply the laws of Pius V, forcing all to profess solemn vows and to observe the cloister. It was only gradually and only after a long period of time that congregations of women were acknowledged by Rome. The history of their recognition by the Church may be summed up briefly in this manner; at first forbidden and opposed, then tolerated, later praised, and only after more than two centuries were they formally approved by Rome."[12]

No new prohibitions were issued in the next few centuries and new congregations of women sprang up. The popes, aware of them, accepted them. "They may have realized the good done by these new communities in the form of charity, for the communities which arose in the seventeenth and eighteenth centuries were most remarkable for their practical character.[13] In 1727, Benedict XIII in his Bull, *Pretiosus,* expressed himself as not wishing to prohibit Tertiaries with simple vows, and in so doing he implicitly approved them. These congregations, nevertheless, remained under the jurisdiction of the Ordinary of the diocese. Even these privileges were short lived, however, being revoked by Benedict's successor, Clement XII.

Mother McAuley's office with first copy of the Rule

It remained for Benedict XIV, recognized as a great canonist, if not the greatest, to clarify in 1794 the issue for all times in his constitution, *Quamvis Justo*. The Holy See without approving the Institute as such would approve the Rules of these Institutes should it see fit. These congregations were now at liberty to approach Rome without fear of being suppressed or of having the cloister imposed, and were free to take simple vows. No further dissenting voices were heard following the ruling of Benedict XIV.

During this period of fluctuation were founded, among other communities of religious women, the two whose Constitutions served as the pattern for Mother McAuley. The Ursulines were founded in 1544 by St. Angela Merici with a Constitution based on that of St. Augustine. By a Brief issued in 1612 by Paul V the Monastery of St. Ursula of Paris observed enclosure and the nuns pronounced solemn vows. In addition to the regulations governing the three religious vows, the Constitution provided detailed instruction for what was considered the special aim of the Order and for which a fourth vow was taken: the instruction of young girls.

The Foundress of the Presentation Sisters, Nano Nagle, was born in County Cork but was educated in Paris. On returning to Ireland she remained in Dublin for a short period of time. It is believed that while here she met Teresa Mullaly, the future builder of George's Hill, assisted her in instructing the poor and meanwhile developed an interest in visiting the sick. Correspondence shows that Nano had returned to Cork prior to 1769 where she established a school of her own for poor girls. She soon recognized that if permanency was to mark her undertaking it needed the stability of a religious group of women. The next ten years of her life were spent seeking such a community. She equipped a convent and brought a band of Ursulines to Cork only to find that they intended to continue their practice of enclosure and education of the better classes. Nano Nagle continued her work with the poor. In December, 1775, encouraged by the Reverend Dr. Francis Moylan, she and a

few companions laid the foundation for what was to be a
new religious congregation. The title selected at this time
was Sisters of the Charitable Instruction of the Sacred Heart
of Jesus.

While considering a number of Rules she was attracted
especially by that of Les Soeurs Grises or the Grey Nuns.
Yet she accepted as a purely *ad hoc* arrangement an adaptation made by the curé of St. Sulpice of the rule of Les Filles
des Ecoles Chrétiennes et Charitables du Saint Enfant Jesus.
Neither this rule in the original nor in the adapted form by
the new congregation included the visitation of the sick. The
preoccupation was education alone. Nevertheless, "up to
Nano's death in 1784, the visitation of the sick was an important but *secondary* duty of the Sisters of Charitable Instruction. Nano Nagle died in 1784 without having made any
ultimate choice of rule for her sisterhood."[14]

The first Brief of the Community at Cork dated September 3, 1791, authorized the erection of convents for the education of young girls and the visitation of sick women in
public infirmaries, the taking of simple vows, and the observance of the rule and constitutions approaching that of
the Institute of St. Ursula but conformable to the needs of
the new congregation.

"Between 1784 and 1791-93," however, "a lessening
premium was set on visitation of the sick. Whatever the
views of Mother Angela Collins [Nano Nagle's successor]
may have been on the subject, the task was impossible
through sheer lack of numbers."[15] In 1800 the remaining six
members of the community asked the Bishop, Reverend Dr.
Moylan, to allow them to appeal for the observance of
enclosure. While Dr. Moylan at first strenuously opposed this
change he gradually conceded to their wishes. This was the
origin of the Brief dated April 9, 1805, which raised the
congregation to a religious order permitting the taking of
solemn vows and obliging the observance of enclosure. In
this Brief a new name appeared for the sisterhood: "Under
the Title and Invocation of the Presentation of the Blessed

Virgin Mary."[16] The Presentation Rule, then, excluded the visitation of the sick inasmuch as the sisters were cloistered. It was this rule that Mother McAuley saw lived at George's Hill and which she subsequently accepted in writing her own.

Before the Congregation of the Sisters of Mercy was four years old the Archbishop of Dublin, Dr. Murray, received word that the reigning Pontiff, Gregory XVI, declared truly worthy of his paternal benevolence and apostolic benediction, and approved the establishment of the new society having for its special end "helping the poor and relieving the sick in every way, and safeguarding, by the exercise of charity, women who find themselves in circumstances dangerous to virtue."[17] It is not surprising that in view of the active apostolate His Holiness "decided that in the present state of affairs it would not be opportune to agree to the proposal that the ladies who are admitted into the Society make solemn vows."[18] In addition to the Presentation Rule it was left to the archbishop to prescribe such observances as necessary for the particular objects of the new congregation.

The choice of a rule had been one of the first concerns of Mother McAuley. This was evident from her letters and the memoirs written by the sisters. Mother Mary Clare Moore, who it will be remembered entered Baggot Street prior to Catherine's sojourn at George's Hill, wrote: "With the permission of the Archbishop, she sent to different convents a request for the loan of their Rule, which she carefully reviewed and read aloud to those who were to form the Institute. All chose the Presentation."[19] Sister Mary Clare Augustine gave this further information: "Dr. Blake procured for her the Rules of all the Religious Houses near Dublin, except that of the [Irish or Mother Aikenhead's] Sisters of Charity . . ."[20] The recording of this latter fact is noted only because of its value in confirming the originality of the chapter in the Mercy Constitutions pertaining to the visitation of the sick.

Historians can be grateful to the memoirs of Mother M. Clare Moore for continuing the story of the writing of the rule with some detail. Dr. Murray confided to Dr. Gaffney of Maynooth the charge of assisting Mother Catherine in adapting the Presentation Rule to her own Institute. In the parent archives in Dublin is a rule signed by the Archbishop and dated "23rd of Jan. 1837." The free page before the table of contents has this inscription: "First copy of our Rule written by Mother McAuley and corrected by His Grace the Most Reverend Dr. Murray in his own handwriting." The corrections are minor with the chapter on enclosure being deleted.[21] The enclosure of the Sisters of Mercy was to be an interior one, or as expressed by Faber: "Charity is their enclosure, while for the love of their Heavenly Spouse, in His poor and suffering members, they deny themselves the peace and protection of a cloister."[22] Mother M. Clare Moore made this reference to the writing of the rule by Mother McAuley:

"Some months later she received directions to forward to Rome those additions to the Presentation Rule which were deemed necessary in order to adapt it to our Institute duties. She sent the chapters [Three: on the Visitation of the Sick, and Four: on the Protection of Women] which she had previously submitted to the Archbishop who then desired her to include them with the Rule, altered as she considered necessary, and to send him a copy of it. Our Foundress transcribed it herself."[23]

The originals of these two chapters are on file in the Sacred Congregation of Propaganda and photostatic copies have been made. In a letter from the parent house in Dublin it was stated: "Our Vice Postulator never had any doubt that the Chapters three and four were the work of our Holy Foundress."[24]

Correspondence during the year 1839 indicated that Mother McAuley's next concern was to have the rule approved by Rome. She wrote to one of the bishops of a diocese in which she had established a convent:

"The Bishop prepared our Rule, and finding it after due trial well suited to our purpose, we now seek its final confirmation in form of a petition from ourselves, a memorial or request from His Grace and all the recommendations we can obtain from our prelates. The Primate has given his in very gratifying terms and Doctor Kinsela has enclosed me a letter to His Holiness, though we are not in either diocese. We take all our documents to London on Monday next and trust you will be so kind to add the tribute of your appreciation."[25]

A rough draft of the petition to which Mother McAuley referred in the letter still exists. Bishop Murphy of Cork suggested introducing into the Act of Profession after the words, "poverty, chastity, and obedience," the clause, "and the service of the poor, sick, and ignorant." This the Foundress did.[26]

The year 1840 and the first half of 1841 were months of anxious waiting. Inquiries during this period were made concerning the status of the community, and to answer these Mother McAuley wrote with some detail:

"Dr. Murray obtained the full approbation of His Holiness for our Order in the year 1835. When His Grace compiled the Rule and when it was completed he affixed his seal and signature; but we did not ask a confirmation of it from the Holy See until we reduced it to practice. When I was in London last January, a petition to that effect was presented, accompanied by letters of strong recommendation from Dr. Murray (Dublin), Dr. Murphy (Cork), Dr. Ryan (Limerick), Dr. Haley (Carlow), Dr. Crolly (Primate), Dr. Kinsela (Kilkenny), Dr. Cantwell (Tullamore), Dr. Griffiths (London). Rev. Dr. Colgan of the Carmelite Order, Dublin, was the bearer of a most gracious answer. He wrote to me to say that if he could remain some time longer he would carry home the documents. I spoke with Dr. Cullen, President of the Irish College at Rome, when in Dublin last summer. He said it was certainly granted but that they were slow in issuing final documents."[27]

Other letters made short references: "It is, however, certain that the process of examination has been gone through and most strong promises made for the conclusion."[28] The Rules and Constitutions as presented were confirmed by Pope Gregory XVI on June 6, 1841, but word did not reach Baggot Street for several months. On August 16 the Foundress wrote to the same sister: "I was aware the confirmation of the Rule was granted, but I have not received it yet—probably His Grace may bring it on Thursday to the ceremony."[29] Who can doubt that when the copy of confirmation was placed in her hands the sentiments of her heart were those of Simeon chanting his Nunc Dimittis!

An edition of this rule was published in Dublin in 1863 and examined by Msgr. Forde, C.S. who certified:

"I have examined carefully this translation of the rule and constitutions of the Sisters of Mercy, and, having compared it with the original, certify that it is substantially accurate. I would recommend, however, that the better to decide any doubts, or questions that may arise, the Italian original should be printed along with it."[30]

According to Mother M. Clare Moore's memoirs the Italian translation was the work of Father Colgan who presented it to the Sacred Congregation of Propaganda in Rome.

Chapter I dealt with the Object of the Congregation beginning:

"1. The Sisters admitted to this Religious Congregation, besides attending particularly to their own perfection, which is the principal end of all religious Orders, should also have in view what is the peculiar characteristic of this Congregation, i.e., the most assiduous application to the Education of poor Girls, the Visitation of the Sick, and the Protection of poor Women of good character."[31]

Chapters III and IV were devoted to the last two works. Chapter III, or the Visitation of the Sick was introduced by mercy:

"1. Mercy—the principal path marked out by Jesus Christ for those who desire to follow Him—has, in all ages of the Church, excited the faithful in a particular manner to instruct and comfort the sick and dying poor—as in them they regarded the person of our Divine Master, Who has said: 'Amen, I say to you, as long as you did it to one of these My least brethren, you did it to me.' "[32]

After a number of paragraphs devoted to proper spiritual motivation Mother McAuley outlined particulars:

"4. The Sisters appointed by the Mother Superior to visit the sick, shall prepare quickly, and, when ready, shall visit the Blessed Sacrament to offer to their Divine Master the action they are about to perform, and to ask from Him the grace necessary to promote His glory, and the salvation of souls."[33]

Later, in her instructions she reminded her listeners: "Remember, there is a great deal less said in the rule on visiting the sick than on the manner of visiting them."[34]

3. Mercy Among the Sick

The question which remains is to determine where Mother McAuley acquired her interest and gained her experience in caring for the sick. There were no nursing schools in her age and the professional nurse as the term is used today did not exist. Catherine had found herself frequently in the midst of persons who were ill and for whom she cared: her own mother, Mr. and Mrs. Callaghan, later her sister Mary, and during a final brief illness, her brother-in-law.

Before leaving Coolock House, during the interval in which Catherine was considering her future, she brought into her home a mentally disturbed woman who had been alone. Catherine cared for her over a period of several years. The only recompense of which the patient was capable was abuse for her benefactor. In 1826 Catherine spent a fortnight at the bedside of Father Nugent who was suffering from typhus fever. Only his death put an end to her twenty-four hour shifts of nursing. Two years later, after Catherine had taken up her residence at the House of Mercy, she did the same for Father Armstrong. It was on this occasion that he gave her as his dying advice: "Place your trust in no human being but in God alone."

Catherine had the added advantage of being surrounded by a family of medical men and pharmacists. The apothecary of that day was accustomed to the practice of some medicine, with the emerging struggle between the two groups occupying the attention of the medical journals, such as the *Lancet*, of that period. Her uncle, her brother-in-law, and brother were doctors; Mr. Armstrong and Mr. Callaghan were what today would be termed pharmacists. Through these associations she learned to know personally the leading members of these professions. These connections were invaluable to her when Catherine undertook a work unfamiliar to post-Reformation and post-Council of Trent days: the visitation of the sick in public hospitals by religious. Was it that God delayed her religious vocation until the groundwork had been laid for a project which would have been inaccessible to her had she been a religious?

Catherine McAuley was interested in caring for the sick poor wherever they were to be found. Many were in their homes because of prevailing conditions.

"For centuries the Poor Law authorities, who came into
existence in the reign of Queen Elizabeth, made no provision
for institutional treatment of the sick. The report of the Poor
Law Commission of 1832-34 hardly mentions the sick poor,
only assuming that they shall receive outdoor relief, and
from 1834 to 1837 no orders were made which changed the
existing practice by which the sick poor were treated in their
own homes."[35]

Catherine and her companions visited them there.

Others would be sought in the hospitals. Meager as was
the care provided for the physical needs of these patients
it was rich indeed in comparison with the consideration
shown for their emotional and spiritual needs. Long before
the term T.L.C. or "tender loving care" was coined, Mother
McAuley made these suggestions for the care of a patient:

"Give her all the care you can for a little time. She is so
gentle it will be no difficult matter to please her—a little
broiled meat or whatever she can take—not to get up till
breakfast time except you have Mass and that she feels able
—not to go out except she likes to try a short walk—great
tenderness of all things."[36]

The first hospital that Catherine visited was that of Sir
Patrick Dun's founded in 1808. This was her first choice
because "one of her Protestant friends was head physician
there."[37] A recent author writing an undocumented article
has named him Dr. James McMahon.[38] Doctor D. John Corrigan, as a medical student under the tutelage of Dr. O'Kel-
ley, attended clinical lectures and spent some practice time
at this hospital. Later, he cared for some of the sisters.

Mercer's Hospital was visited next. Opened in 1734 and
named after its founder, Mary Mercer, this hospital for
many years

"received its main support from the proceeds of concerts of sacred music given by "The Charitable and Musical Society." In the hospital Minute Book of 1741 appears a record of the first public performance of the MESSIAH given when the illustrious Handel 'came to try his fortune in the Irish capital.' "[39]

Steeven's Hospital, the third to be added in 1828 to the list for regular visitations, is of special interest because of the resident physician, Dr. Abraham Colles, who served in that capacity from 1798 to 1842. Dr. Colles was one of a group of men whose influences were such as to leave their mark in medical history. Remembered most readily, perhaps, for his description in 1814 of the fracture of the wrist known as Colles' fracture, Dr. Colles' contributions to the medicine of his day were enhanced by his professorship in anatomy and surgery at the College of Surgeons, a position he held for thirty-two years.[40] He has been called the Morning Star of the Dublin School of Medicine.[41]

Under these circumstances the historian may well ask whether Dr. Colles and Mother McAuley worked in cooperation as physician and nurse in the following situation:

"On one occasion, being requested by a clergyman to visit a young lady who had come to Dublin to have a surgical operation performed on her knee, [Catherine McAuley] had such compassion on her friendless position, that she had her removed to the House in Baggot Street, where she nursed her with maternal care. During the amputation, she remained with her to assist and comfort her; and she was all the more attentive, as the patient received all her care as a matter of course, and did not evince the slightest gratitude. She even left Mother McAuley to pay all the expenses occasioned by her illness, and these were considerable, as many physicians and surgeons held lengthened consultations before the operation was performed."[42]

By the time Catherine had gone to George's Hill,

Georgina Moore, later Mother M. Clare, recorded the names of two other hospitals which they visited: the Incurable Hospital at Donnybrook and the Lying-In Hospital at the Coombe. Here and at the Steeven's Hospital they may have met Sir Philip Crampton, Consulting Surgeon to both hospitals, who later cared for the sisters.

In the March following Mother McAuley's return to Baggot Street the plague of Asiatic cholera, spreading westward, had reached Ireland. In early April the Grangegorman penitentiary in Dublin was equipped to care for cholera patients to be attended by Mother Aikenhead's Sisters of Charity. By the twenty-third of April the Board of Health recognized the need for small hospitals established in key positions throughout the city. As a result the Townsend Street Depot was converted into a cholera hospital with a request from the Board of Health that Mother McAuley take charge of it. The appeal came to her the day that her George's Hill companion, Sister M. Elizabeth, died on April 25, 1832. "Reverend Mother felt her loss most sensibly; but her own feelings had long been under perfect control."[43] She wrote the Archbishop immediately for permission to go to Townsend Street. He called at the convent that same evening, and after conferring with the Foundress, addressed himself to the sisters adding his own entreaties on behalf of the afflicted.

"One and all [the sisters] offered to go wherever their services were wanted; and throwing themselves on their knees before him, received his parting advice and blessing. They left their house that very day, and took up their abode entirely in the public hospitals. There they continued during the prevalence of the calamity, attending the sick, performing towards them those kind offices which they required, enabling them by their sympathy to bear their sufferings with patience, and in the agony of their last moments inspiring them with sentiments of religious resignation."[44]

Early chroniclers wrote of the calming effect which the

presence of the sisters had upon the cholera victims. The praise appears less exaggerated when weighed against other contemporary accounts of the panic which prevailed. Dr. Howison from Scotland visited Ireland in August, 1832, and wrote his impressions:

"At Sligo, of 18,000 inhabitants, the population of the town, in a few days 16,000 fled from the place, in terror— the wealthiest families paying 40 or 50 pounds sterling for a small room in the country to live in—the poorer classes living with their families under canvass, while others slept in the woods and under the hedges.

"At Enniskillen, of eight medical practitioners in that town, two died. One left the place, having previously lost his sister from cholera.

"No individual who was not present, or dwelling in such places, can form an idea to what an extent fear and imagination acted upon the minds of the people; so much so that even the affection between one relation and another gave way to self-preservation."[45]

Bleeding was the treatment which the above author indicated was used for the first stage of the cholera followed by the use of calomel, and opium in large quantities. Articles which appeared in the *Lancet* by other physicians during the next few years show that the advisability of using calomel came to be questioned. At Townsend Street "brandy, laudanum and heating applications were the ordinary remedies."[46]

Among the medical men with whom Mother Catherine worked at the cholera hospital were the head physician, Dr. Hart, and Dr. Andrew Furlong. On the testimony of the latter, Dr. Hart stated that the sisters "were of the greatest use, and that the hospital could not be carried on without them." His own interpretation was that the head physician gave Mother McAuley fullest control, held long consultations with her, and attributed the small percentage of deaths (about 30 per cent), in comparison with the usual high percentage, to her wise administration.

The sisters relieved each other in groups of four going to the hospital early in the morning and remaining until late in the evening, but Mother Catherine "scarcely left the hospital the entire day, though she had the remainder of the Community relieve each other every four hours."[47] By June the cholera had subsided sufficiently in Dublin for the Board of Health to anounce that the Grangegorman hospital would be closed on the fifteenth, but that the smaller Town-street Hospital would be kept open for the reception of malignant cases. The Sisters of Mercy continued to care for the patients at Townsend Street until December. By that time the disease had run its course; the Board of Health Report for the fourteenth stated: "On account of the decline of the cholera the daily reports will now stop. Weekly reports only will be issued."[48]

God had spared the sisters from falling victims to the cholera. But they did become ill despite the "port wine and mutton chops" recommended by Archbishop Murray as an addition to their spare diet when he sent the sisters to nurse the victims of the plague.[49]

"Reverend Mother, who notwithstanding her love of austerities, was always most kind to the sick, did her best to restore them. The Surgeon General, the late Sir P. Crampton, was called in, I forget to which of them, and he having always less faith in medicine than management, inquired into their food and occupations. At once he declared that an amelioration of the diet would be the best cure, and especially he ordered beer. He tried to convince Reverend Mother of the real unwholesomeness of the visitation, but she never could understand and always maintained that fresh air must be good, forgetting that it must be taken by us mostly in Townsend Street and Bull Alley. . . . Sir P.

Crampton also said that the silence religious observed at meals was unwholesome, so more recreation days were appointed than she afterwards found convenient."[50]

Seven years later Mother McAuley had occasion to refer to Sir Crampton in a letter:

"I suppose you heard of Father Carroll's death. Since it was the holy will of God to call him, there is every reason to rejoice in the pity and mercy which rescued him from sudden death and protracted decline. Dr. Crampton said he would linger some months."[51]

Sir Philip Crampton (1777-1858) had formed a friendship with Dr. Cheyne when the two had served in the army, and the friendship continued for many years benefiting the latter when he settled in Dublin. Sir Philip was a prolific writer. In 1834 he presented before the Royal College of Surgeons an outline of the history of medicine which was developed and published in 1839. In this year Queen Victoria raised him to the dignity of Baronet of the United Kingdom. Records indicate that he was too sensitive ever to give pain to others and that he had respect for the less fortunate. This would claim for him Mother McAuley's regard. It claimed the regard, likewise, of his profession for at his death was written:

"In a purely Medical and Surgical Journal it is, of course, chiefly with Sir Philip's professional character we have to deal. This notice would, however, be imperfect were we to pass over in total silence the kindliness of disposition, the affectionate sympathy, particularly for those who, rich or poor, required his skillful aid, which endeared him to all classes; nor do we see why the testimony of one of his servants should not be recorded:—"I have lived with him for three and thirty years, and never did I hear a cross word from his lips."[52]

The first case of cholera in the Dublin epidemic was reported by Dr. William Stokes.[53] His is one of a trinity of names carrying forward the reputation begun by Colles for the Irish school of medicine. The other two are Robert James Graves and Dominic John Corrigan.

"Graves' name is indelibly attached to the disease known as exopthalmic goitre, which he described and separated from other affections before anyone else had realized its individuality. William Stokes was, perhaps, the best authority on diseases of the heart and lungs in his time. His name will be preserved in the designation of the peculiar form of breathing which occurs in certain comatose conditions and has received the name Cheyne-Stokes respiration, in honor of the men who first called attention to it. Corrigan was in his time one of the greatest authorities on the heart, and especially of the pulse. His name is preserved in the term Corrigan pulse, which is applied to a peculiar condition that occurs very characteristically in disease of the aortic valves of the heart."[54]

These three men were known by Mother McAuley; also, they took care of her sisters and subsequently herself. In evaluating them she used dimensions not limited by nationality or religion. Of Dr. Corrigan, the only one of the three who was of pure Irish ancestry, and who remained throughout life a sincere Catholic, she wrote in 1840: "Dr. Corrigan thinks Booterstown as good air for [Sister M. Aloysius] as any other. She is gone there."[55] And a month later: "From the letters sent me I expected to find Sister Aloysius near death and three others very bad. She looks exceedingly thin and pale, has no cough, is now in Booterstown which Dr. Corrigan prefers for her to any other air."[56] Sister M. Aloysius recovered and was appointed superior for the foundation to Birr. A year later, in the summer of 1841, Mother Catherine wrote concerning a novice, Sister M. Justina: "Her father sent Dr. Corrigan to attend her in Booterstown. She has been blistered, leeched, and kept on a low diet. The strength is greatly exhausted."⁵⁷ To another she wrote confidentially a few days later: "Dr. Corrigan attending at her father's request. He would not have been our choice. Let not a word contained in this letter reach an ear that would carry it to the world."⁵⁸ After more than a century the world may well pause to ask, "Why would he not have been Mother McAuley's choice?"

Medical history indicates that Dr. Corrigan's specialty centered around heart conditions. From the letters written to others it is clear that the novice was suffering from "consumption" and, except for the air, the treatment used by Dr. Corrigan in this instance was not that more commonly advocated by his confreres for tuberculosis. There may have been other factors, though, which had equal influence. In his earlier years Dr. Corrigan apparently was not as tactful as he might have been and because of this was rejected at one time for honorary membership in the Irish College of Physicians. His was a long life and eventually he was to know honor among all the scientific groups of his day. But these gifts came in a forty-year span when Mother McAuley was gone.

"He came to have one of the largest practices that any practitioner in Dublin, or for that matter in any city of the world, has ever enjoyed, if enjoyment it can be called. His office used to be crowded with patients who would occupy all his time if he allowed them to do so. In order to secure opportunities for his other work, for his lectures, for his hospital visitation, and for his pathological investigation, he had a back entrance to his house through which he could steal out—even though there were many patients waiting for him—when he felt that it was time for him to fill another engagement."⁵⁹

The Foundress would have been the first to concede that it does not follow that the patient is the physician's master even though the physician is the servant of the patient. Yet it is very doubtful whether her choice of method in accomplishing the end desired would have been that used by the eminent physician.

Her own preferences point to Doctors Graves and Stokes. In 1836 she wrote:

"We have been seriously alarmed about dear Sister [Rose] Luby and thought we were going to pay our annual tribute to the tomb, but this day, thanks be to God, there is a more favorable opinion—though strong symptoms of rapid consumption appear. Her brother appointed Dr. Graves to visit her and his treatment has been quite different from what we have seen on similar melancholy occasions. So far it has been wonderfully successful and we have great hope."[60]

What was the treatment to which Mother McAuley referred? Histories of medicine show that Dr. Graves initiated more than one new treatment. He held that the emaciation and weakness accompanying prolonged fever was due to restricted diets, and in an era when intravenous therapy was unknown, stressed that fever patients must be fed regularly whether they had an appetite or not. More important, perhaps, was his recognition for the need of a properly qualified nurse to care for these patients.

"Dr. Graves felt very deeply that the most important element in the treatment is the conservation of the patient's strength with the preservation of his morale, and this can be best accomplished when the patient is constantly under the care of an experienced nurse, noting every symptom and averting every possible source of worry and every form of exhaustion of energy."[61]

This was treatment prescribed before the advent of the professional nurse and the concentration on the phrase: total patient care. Dr. Graves recognized his patients as persons.

The rich knew his skill; the poor appreciated his tenderness. And Mother McAuley gravitated to anyone who loved the poor.

The man associated with Dr. Graves not only professionally but also as a personal friend was Dr. Stokes. He did much to publicize the use of the stethoscope and to further Laennec's recent discovery of auscultation. With Cheyne, a Scottish physician who had settled in Dublin, he immortalized the Cheyne-Stokes respiratory combination. The book which won him lasting fame dealt with diseases of the heart, but when Mother McAuley knew him he was concerned more with conditions of the chest. Together with Graves, Stokes had definite attitudes concerning the health practices which were best for the person with tuberculosis. The principles differed from what had been customary. Part of the treatment ordered was to spend a large part of the day in the open air, to ride in an open carriage several hours a day if possible, and to avoid tiring.

In the same letter concerning the novice referred to earlier Mother McAuley revealed that Dr. Stokes also was called in to attend Sister M. Justina: "Dr. Stokes, who is now considered the best opinion in lung cases, desires she would drive out every fine day. He says she is better, but fears consumption is lingering."[62] But the time was at hand for Mother McAuley herself to be the patient.

Less than two months before her death she described a visit from Dr. Stokes. Her account serves to illustrate how keenly a patient observes the manner and expression of those around the sick bed, and manifests how lightly the Foundress passed over her own condition so as not to alarm those who would be concerned.

"I am not weak tho' I cannot say I have an appetite. Mr. O'Hanlon particularly requested I would consult Dr. Stokes. I have seen him twice. On his first visit he looked like a person who had made a great discovery. On his second, Mother DiPazzi conducted him out and returned with such sorrow in her countenance that I entreated her to tell me his opinion: 'My lung was diseased.' I have now less confidence than ever in the faculty, and you know my stock was small enough. I do not think my lung is affected. I am now dead to the poor children [her sisters]—not to read, speak, give out office, &&.

"I tell you all these particulars to give you the benefit of experience. If my lung is actually engaged, the progress will not be checked."[63]

Mother Catherine could speak from experience and from her actions it is evident that she was influenced by the doctor's decision. She placed all her things in order quietly and unobtrusively destroying whatever might give an insight into her own interior life. The end came unexpectedly to all but herself. Her last moments were the echo of a life spent for others. "My child," she could whisper to the sister cook, "the poor sisters look greatly fatigued; be sure you have a comfortable cup of tea for them when I am gone."[64]

She had laid the foundations for the care of the sick. Within a few years after her death was realized the fulfillment of the wishes which she had indulged and expressed

"that [the sisters] could have an hospital of their own, in which the poor could have all their wants—spiritual and temporal—perfectly ministered to during their sufferings, and not be obliged to leave till their strength would be quite restored."[65]

Within these walls would be transmitted the spirit of nursing which Catherine McAuley left to her Congregation —a spirit that she considered an integral part of "comfortable arrangements and a sufficient staff of nurses," a spirit characterizing "the services of those who devote themselves to the sick for the love of God."[66]

PART IV

A Spirit Tested

The influence of every religious community may be traced back, in large measure, to the spirit of the founder or foundress. In a recent study of Missouri rural hospitals, Habenstein and Christ, while not in sympathy with all they believe they found existing in Catholic hospitals, were forced to admit that "in one way or another the influence of the order runs through the hospital household from top to bottom."[1] The religious life is a shared attribute of all religious congregations, yet each has a particular spirit which distinguishes it from others.

"Institutions and great movements are personal things. Out from some rich personality they proceed. They achieve a personality of their own. But in the greater and more extensive personality which is theirs, we can still discern the personality from which they emanated: they retain something of the soul and spirit of their foundress. They are a larger body, a more extensive personality, if you will, but the life that is theirs was first the life of a single man or woman. Without some insight into the spirit of that individual man or woman we have no understanding of the institute that sprang like a living thing from their mind and soul."[2]

1. The Spirit of Mercy

It has been said that "the animating principle of the Sister of Mercy is her undying love for our Lord in the per-

In the name of the Father & the Son

+

My God look down with pity and
Mercy. on your afflicted poor and
grant us grace to do all that we can
for their relief and Comfort
we most humbly, ask your blessing
this day — in the name and for
the Sake of our Lord and Saviour
Jesus Christ — Amen

In the name of the Father & the Son.

+

Prayer of Catherine McAuley in own handwriting
(Original, Sisters of Mercy Motherhouse, Burlingame, California)

son of the poor, the sick, and the ignorant."[3] This is implied in the formula of her vows. In Mother McAuley the love of Christ and His afflicted melded into mercy for others. This is the spirit which she committed to her followers. In order to understand the true meaning of mercy and, therefore, her spirit, it is necessary to clarify what is meant by the term poor as also that of mercy to which it may give rise.

Contrary to the general use of the term, "the poor" includes many more than those in financial need. In Our Lord's pronouncement concerning the final judgment He catalogued a variety: the spiritually, mentally, physically, and socially poor as well as the financially poor. It was for all these that Mother Catherine begged God's mercy in a short prayer which exists in her own handwriting:

My God, look down with pity and mercy on your afflicted poor and grant us grace to do all that we can for their relief and comfort. We most humbly ask your blessing this day, in the name and for the sake of Our Lord and Savior Jesus Christ. Amen.[4]

The works which the Foundress instituted announce her all-embracing concept of the poor. Her own words as well attest to this. An instruction given to her novices illustrates spiritual and social needs as aspects of being poor. Speaking to the small group preparing to embrace a vow of poverty, she said:

"Consider the poverty of Jesus Christ on the cross, stripped of His clothes, forsaken by His friends, and even by His Eternal Father. He was silent under His other torments but when *that* interior support was taken from Him, He cried out, "My God, My God, why hast Thou forsaken Me?" (Mark 15:34) The religious soul, considering this great poverty of her dear Saviour, should resolve to bear patiently, if not joyfully, the interior trials she may have to undergo, and also all contempt, privation, and indigence to which her state of life and of poverty are liable."[5]

These interrelated phases of poverty forming a single whole are categorized in the spiritual and corporal works of mercy. With the fulfillment of these is associated the reward which Christ promises to the merciful. What, then, is mercy?

God's mercy is a radiation of His love which respects the weakness of His creatures. For this reason it is fitting that Mary be the dispenser of this mercy. She helps man, as it were, to retain his personal dignity in accepting what lies beyond the domain of justice.

For man, mercy is a moral virtue which prompts the possessor to compassion and to relieve those in any type of want. St. Thomas Aquinas expresses it as "a heart suffering over the sufferings of others. That is more evident in the Latin word for mercy, *Misericordia,* 'sad at heart.' "[6] Marmion calls it "goodness in the face of misery."[7]

Mercy does not reside in the emotions but in the will and should not be confused with feeling. Bede Jarrett stresses this in a manner which is apropos particularly for the professional person:

"Mercy sometimes has to be severe, strong. The hands of a nurse dealing with her patient are merciful hands, not less merciful because they are firm! The poison may have to be pressed out of the wound. Then it is not mercy not to hurt the patient. That is not merciful. That is unmerciful. It looks unkind; it seems unkind; he winces under her action. The body quivers because she will not go. She [applies] strong pressure if there be no other way. To be tender, compassionate, full of mercy, is the very profession of the nurse. Yet that must not undo her firmness. A doctor, again has strong hands, and merciful, because of the very strength of them. His cutting of human flesh is mercy. Mercy must be wise."[8]

Mother Catherine comprehended the true meaning of mercy. She understood it to be not a humanitarian service but one which was supernatural in order and which complemented charity whose superstructure it becomes. Her mercy was wise, it came from a human heart, and it had its source in God. This is apparent in her maxims:

"The charity of God would not avail us if His mercy did not come to our aid. Charity not only requires that we instruct, but also that we should pity, encourage, and even reprove those under our care, as they may require. While we are to serve our neighbor to the best of our ability, we must not expect to [be able to] relieve all his wants, but to regulate our charity according to order. Mercy is more than charity; it not only bestows benefits, but receives anew, and pardons again and again, even the most ungrateful.

"How kind, how charitable, how merciful, ought not Sisters of Mercy to be. The mercy of God comes to our assistance. It is for Him we serve [those in need], not for thanks."9

Such measured words may be weighed against those written about the Foundress when souls in distress were concerned:

"[Her] spirit of mercy and compassion made her, at times, adopt plans for their relief which, to some, appeared to exceed the limits of prudence. The success, however, with which her undertakings were uniformly attended showed that she was guided by heavenly wisdom, and that her works received the blessing of God."10

Mother McAuley's letters reveal the primacy that mercy for the poor held in her day-by-day activities. So frequently cited that she has become identified by them are her words: "[God] knows I would rather be cold and hungry than [that] the poor in Kingstown or elsewhere should be deprived of any consolation in our power to afford."11 Less than a month previously she had written concerning the above situation: "My heart felt sorrowful when I thought of the poor being deprived of the comfort which God seemed to intend for them."[12]

There are many other brief, casual statements having significance because of their spontaneity. To mention only a few: "He was a kind creature to the poor"[13]; "Tell me all the news you have about your school and sick poor"[14]; "Returning from Mass this morning a sweet looking old woman from the country stopped me putting six pennies in my hand. I said, 'For the sick poor.' No, honey, for the Sisters—for yourselves."[15] Such abstracts serve to disclose Catherine as a true social worker: her first concern centering itself on those in need of assistance.

When it came to herself and her sisters her advice was: "The Lord and Master of our house is a faithful provider. Let us never desire more than enough. He will give that and a blessing."[16] She rejoiced when others caught the fire of God's love to place the needs of others above personal gain: "A sixth [sister] has arrived since I came back. They renew my spirit greatly—five creatures fit to adorn society coming forward joyfully to consecrate themselves to the service of the poor for Christ's sake. This is some of the fire He cast upon the earth."[17]

2. The Spirit of Mercy with the Sick

In turning to an analysis of the directives left by Mother McAuley for the care of the sick a cursory reading may leave the impression that a large portion of concerted effort favored the dying patient. This is correct but needs to be evaluated properly. Her visitations took her into homes where illness was accompanied by utter poverty and little or no medical attention. Her own description remains:

"It would be impossible to give a just description of these

scenes of sorrow while in addition to the anguish of death, all around are in want and misery. And even when a poor family are not deprived of their usual support the weak and sick are often found turning away unable to partake of it."[18]

These are restrained words; those of the liberator of Ireland, Daniel O'Connell, are less so:

"The Sisters of Mercy . . . are hastening to the lone couch of some fellow-creature fast sinking into the grave with none to console, none to soothe. They come with consolation and hope, and bring down by their prayers the blessing of God on the dying sinner, on themselves, and on their country."[19]

Catherine McAuley cared for the sick, whether in the home or in the public hospital, more than twenty years before Florence Nightingale and Mother Catherine's own Sisters of Mercy nursed the wounded soldiers in the Crimea, and before the advent of asepsis, anesthesia, or antibiotics. She and her sisters nursed many through a cholera epidemic. In such circumstances attention was focused on the dying. The Foundress spoke freely, therefore, of the importance of assisting patients to prepare for the all-important moment of death.

"Where there is no hope of recovery, charity requires that we make it known gradually and cautiously lest the patient be too much alarmed. We may suggest many motives for resignation, such as the vanity of the world . . .; the happiness of dying in God's grace; the joys of Heaven; the peace experienced by those who are entirely conformed to the will of God.

"We should, moreover, counsel the sick to make frequent acts of abandonment; for once they have been to confession, and are truly contrite, they ought not to indulge fears about eternity; but cast themselves into the ocean of God's mercy, with an humble confidence, trusting to the merits of their Saviour, and the intercession of His Blessed Mother."[20]

The ultimate purpose of any social work instituted by Mother Catherine was to bring men to God. In the care of the sick she made particular note of this objective: "The good of souls is what the Sisters shall have principally in view."[21] This does not detract from the care bestowed upon sick minds and bodies. Rather, to do less would be to fail in caring for the whole patient. God did not create man a disembodied spirit but a social being. Only man communicates and establishes human relationships. This he does through the instrumentality of bodily powers. Reverence and care for that body and a recognition of the interaction upon it of the emotions and mental powers is essential for effective nursing.

The Foundress was aware of the influence of the spoken word. She knew well that there were situations in which words alone were sterile, unless the manner or action indicated a practical belief in the intrinsic dignity of man.

"[The nurse] should act with great tenderness, and . . . it will be well, first, to relieve distress, and to endeavor in every practical way to promote the cleanliness, ease and comfort of the sick person; since we are always better disposed to receive advice and instruction from those who show compassion for us."[22]

Walsh has named this paragraph of the Rule taken from the chapter, "Visitation of the Sick," MOTHER MCAULEY'S CREED OF SERVICE; and with insight calls attention to an important fact:

"The structure of that sentence is typical of the way in which Mother McAuley did her work. In the last portion of it she identifies herself with the poor by using the first person plural 'we'; that is, all of us 'are ever more disposed to receive admonition and instruction from those who show compassion for us.' "[23]

The above commentary may be studied with advantage by anyone caring for the sick. Social psychologists would find in it material for analyzing the Foundress' self-concept and how she related to other members of society.

Where mercy was to be the hallmark there was little place for hard-and-fast rules. "Mother McAuley, while anxious for the most perfect discipline, was careful not to make, as she styled it, 'too many laws,' "[24] adding, "if we draw the strings too tight they will break."[25] Forbearance and judgment were to be the attendants of mercy. In the distribution of relief through what in our age would be called a "Visiting Nurse Service," she advised: "making every inquiry that may lead to a true knowledge of the case. The Sisters carry nourishment and clothing to the sick and very seldom give money except for fire and light."[26] There were no telephone directories and even if there had been the names of those whom these visiting nurses sought undoubtedly would not have been listed. "If some places cannot be found without making inquiries," the Foundress wrote, "it will be most prudent to go to a huxter's or baker's shop, where the poor are generally known; . . . but they should not continue their inquiries, since charity is not only kind but does not behave unseemly."[27] In the instructions given to the young sisters Mother McAuley impressed upon them that the nurse should be "ever complying, ever forbearing, ever charitable, ever compassionate to the weakness and frailties of others."[28] Practice, therefore, knew a wide latitude which was restricted only by available resources and discernment of need: charity regulated by order.

Kindness of manner in caring for the sick was limited by no confining clauses. Mother Catherine emphasized in particular the tone and manner of speaking and gave, as was her custom, the reasons. "Our manner of speaking should be easy, soothing, and impressive, as a loud voice distresses the sick."[29] Another reason given was: "so as not to embarrass or fatigue the poor patient."[30]

This recognition for the social virtues has been developed by Cooke in speaking of the contributions of Mother Mc-Auley to the betterment of society:

"The foundress probably never used the term 'social virtues,' but her words and actions indicate that she appreciated their worth in enhancing human relations, as well as their value in drawing souls to God. Charity was the virtue she most frequently recommended; it was at the root of her own activities and it was the legacy she left her companions. She realized fully, though, that just as a river has many tributaries which flow into it and give it depth, so, too, charity has many ramifications which must be recognized and developed if the virtue is to thrive. Hence, she emphasized such traits as courtesy, sympathy, gentleness, cheerfulness, consideration for others and forgetfulness of self together with a gentle reserve to prevent extremes in behavior. She also considered obedience, docility, and respect for authority requirements for the promotion of unity and charity. She realized that all people consciously or unconsciously are seeking happiness, and their search is being carried on in close proximity with their fellow men. Therefore each one helps or hinders others along the way, depending on whether he selflessly strives to assist others or selfishly ignores their rights."[31]

The counseling techniques of today had not been defined. But knowing the human heart long before psychologists concerned themselves with men's conflicts and frustrations, the Foundress could say that "it unburdens the mind of some, to make known all their little trials; and thus, it is well to listen to them, in order to gain their confidence, and to draw them to God."[32] Does the passive participation of the good listener with the ultimate gaining of confidence imply that the "client" found a solution to his problem? Or, in another instance, did the verbalizing help him to learn that Our Lord was the Counselor par excellence? For Catherine McAuley the real counselor was He to whom she recommended the adviser to have recourse: "We should add a fervent prayer [to] Our Lord, the true Changer of hearts."[33]

The leadership which the nurse is called upon to assume in the nurse-patient relationship may profit from the permissive climate created by this nineteenth-century educator whose respect for the individual as a person was opposed to action based merely on the leader's choosing. The Foundress who advised a "gentle, unassuming"[34] role sensed the cooperation resulting when both parties possessed a common goal, and the importance of establishing the rapport that would help the patient discover those spiritual and social outcomes which were best for himself. For the nurse to respond in a therapeutic manner, so as to develop supporting attitudes in the patient, she must have an insight or awareness into herself and manifest behavior which denotes self-possession. As a guide to the prudent application of control Mother Catherine wrote:

"Authority should be exercised in such a manner as to convince the person over whom it is exercised that the necessity of being in authority is painful. If we have to refuse a request, it should be done decidedly but mildly, showing the impossibility or disadvantage of acceding. We should always let it be seen that we would feel much happier if we could grant the request."[35]

In culling Mother McAuley's letters to see whether a similar spirit reveals itself in dealing with her sisters on the new foundations, statements such as these are found: "I leave you free to do what you think best."[36] And again: "Never suppose you can make me feel displeased by giving any opinion that occurs to you."[37]

The theme song of nursing at the moment is the care of the whole patient—or total patient care. The nurse is told that this includes a litany of unexpressed needs in addition to those which are physical, or upon which the physical demands may be based, and that comprehensive nursing embraces family needs. Mother McAuley, to whom the poor meant anyone with a need, said simply:

"There are things the poor prize more highly than gold, though they cost the donor nothing; among these are the kind word, the gentle, compassionate look, and the patient hearing of their sorrows."[38]

Certainly she did what was in her power to relieve their problems and knew when to refer them to others for help. In her estimation all these were basic to good nursing. Without their balancing influence, total patient care did not exist.

3. *Theocentric Motivation*

In this mid-twentieth century values are being tossed about in a somewhat nebulous fashion. In the hierarchy of good, God, whom St. Thomas calls the Supreme Good, is omitted completely by many in their scale of values. Mother McAuley would have attributed to God, in today's terminology, the master value. The Pauline ideal of being "all things to all men" (I Corinthians 9:22) had its counterpart in her because her life was centered in God. The Mystical Body with its suffering members was for her a reality. She found God in the person of her neighbor. And inasmuch as charity begins at home she found Him first in those about her and then, because good diffuses itself, she went out to seek Him in the market place of the world.

"In her the Spirit of Christ went out in love and tenderness and mercy to the Christ who had imprisoned Himself in the very poor [and that includes the sick].

"As proof of that I offer you, in addition to the external life of mercy, the dominant object of her inner life [which] was charity. . . . That reveals the inner mind of Mother McAuley. Her aim was charity, not only towards the poor, but towards those around her. She was a practical woman. She saw the fundamental fact that those who love Jesus Christ must love Him where He is. . . . If we discover Christ in those around us, we shall find Him the more easily in the poor."[39]

Are these words mere oratory? Or do they echo what the Foundress herself taught? In the *Constitutions* she described briefly what the manner of the nurses should be on their way to the homes of the sick: "Preserving recollection of mind as if they expected to meet their Divine Redeemer in every habitation."[40] More detail was given in her instructions.

"By our vocation . . . we are engaged to comfort and instruct the sick poor of Christ.

"This is the principal reason why we [bear the title] of Mercy, and why, to the faithful discharge of this duty so many graces are annexed. . . . Oh! what an ineffable consolation to serve Christ Himself, in the person of the poor, and to walk in the very same path which He trod!

"Our hearts should be replenished with love and gratitude . . . for allowing us so graciously to aid Him in the person of the poor . . .

"Our very looks should bespeak recollection, and this will be the case, if we expect to meet our Divine Redeemer in each habitation."[41]

By empathy man enters into the feelings of another. A century and a quarter ago Catherine McAuley, pioneering in nursing, counseled "evident and sincere concern" in ministering to the sick "for if our own hearts be not moved, in vain shall we hope to move the hearts of others."[42] The interpersonal relations which she practiced were the external manifestations of her love for God whom she served in others. "This exterior," she would admonish the group she was instructing, "can never be obtained without interior sanctity, far more valuable than the exterior of which it is only the emblem and effect."[43]

The Foundress knew only too well that unaided human nature would find it difficult at times to care for the ungrateful and the sick. To make it easier for the nurse to relate in these circumstances she reminded her sisters and through them the nurses they teach that each "should view Jesus Christ in those she relieves, instructs, converses with, or assists in any way, for He has said, 'Amen, I say to you, as long as you did it for one of these, the least of my brethren, you did it for me.' (Matt. 25:40)."[44] She herself demonstrated what she taught by word, and observed others while they learned. To do so Mother Catherine, in the role of clinical instructor, accompanied these early visiting nurses on their first trips into the homes of the sick. She wished them grounded in the fundamentals of nursing and in the important WHY, the basic principle underlying all relationships with self and others: "God's image is impressed on their souls, which are washed in the Precious Blood of Christ."[45]

Tyler[46] listed two chief characteristics of a profession. The second, or the use of techniques that are based upon principles, involves judgment and identification of aspects requiring adaptations to these principles. The Foundress' practice of acting on principle and her ability to adapt is interwoven into this chapter. The first characteristic listed by Tyler, the existence of a recognized code of ethics, places social values above selfish ones, together with a dedication on the part of the individual to these higher values. Bixler and Bixler believed that "a profession attracts individuals of intellectual and professional qualities who exalt service above personal gain and who recognize their chosen occupation as a life work."[47] To measure the stature of Mother McAuley against this mark of professionalism and to bestow upon her the accolade of nurse educator, the words of her early biographer are cited first:

"There was nothing of self about her, but she made everything in her conduct subservient to God's honor and the neighbor's good. For these, and these alone, she conversed, and worked, and lived."[48]

Her own testimony of self-forgetfulness was written unknowingly about three months before her death. Read the answer made in sincere charity to an invitation to accept the effects of Carlow air in the hope that her distressing cough would improve by the change, a method she often resorted to for others in a similar condition:

"I am sure I need not say it would be delightful to accept the invitation to St. Leo's but think of all that must be left behind. . . . It is quite impossible for anyone in my situation to think of pleasing themselves. My pleasure must be in endeavouring to please all."[49]

Her words keep alive a spirit of dedicated service. Freedom and pleasure-loving young women still experience joy and satisfaction in the knowledge that one day they may hear the reward of charity: "Come . . . I was hungry, thirsty, sick, and homeless . . . and you did it to Me."

This total concept of nursing has been paraphrased concisely in a recent description of nursing:

"In keeping with the spirit of Mother Mary Catherine McAuley, nursing is regarded not as mere professional service, but as a gracious work of mercy in which the nurse ministers to Christ in the poor, the sick, and the suffering."[50]

An adaptation of this statement built upon its underlying philosophy could be expressed in this way: For the nurse imbued with the spirit of Mother Mary Catherine McAuley, nursing, whether of a professional or semiprofessional nature, is a work of mercy disciplined by a specialized body of knowledge and the practice of social relationships which characterize the nurse as ministering to Christ in those whom she serves.

4. Theocentric Influences in Nursing

Emerging from Mother Catherine's theocentric motivation are myriad qualities which characterize her. Many pertain to her interior life. Others have a special place in the education of the nurse if she is to reflect the true image of Mother McAuley in nursing. Whether the mercy nurse steps out into the community to assume her role in the prevention of illness and the return to health or remains in the hospital, Mother McAuley continues the relief of the sick through her. The Foundress depends on the nurse of today to bring to the world a prodigality of mercy worthy to be offered again to Christ. An understanding of these traits will help the nurse in her own development and in adapting herself to the social unit of which she is a member.

Mother Catherine, as has been shown, was careful not to work for earthly thanks. Nevertheless, gratitude for favors received she stressed and practiced. She was grateful, first, to God and inculcated a like gratitude in others.

"Let those whom Jesus Christ has graciously permitted to assist Him in the suffering Poor, have their hearts animated with gratitude and love, and placing all their confidence in Him, ever keep His unwearied patience and humility present to their minds."[51]

She acknowledged, likewise, the many favors which came to her community through men's hands. Her letters reveal her concern that these kindnesses should not be forgotten when time normally might erase them from memory. In addition to perpetuating the names of living and deceased benefactors in the Annals of each community,[52] the Sisters of Mercy offer special Mass intentions praying God to bless those who assist them in their work for the afflicted.

The Foundress regarded priests as benefactors in a special way. They were protectors to her Institute; and through them came the graces of the Sacraments and of the Holy Sacrifice of the Mass. The basis for her reverence for the priesthood, according to her biographer, was a veneration which extended to everything connected with religion. Whether the priest favored or opposed her cause, she did not lose sight of the sanctity of his state and taught all to evince toward him respect by word and manner.[53] For the nurse this has related meaning in the courtesy and reverence she shows God's ordained representative; in her observation that the patient and his environment are prepared for his visits and for the administration of the Sacraments; and in her recognition of his position on the health team.

Mother McAuley's devotion to the Blessed Sacrament and to the Passion of our Divine Lord were the source of her strength and went hand in hand with her devotion to His Sacred Heart. As such each constituted an important part in her instructions to her followers. After giving emphasis to each in particular the Foundress appeared to summarize their unity in a few paragraphs:

"The very institution of the Blessed Eucharist, and the sufferings which Jesus endured in His dolorous passion and death, owed their origin to the burning love which inflamed His Sacred Heart.

"The loving Heart of our Divine Spouse on earth, so laden with the sorrows of His humanity, in heaven, so overflowing with the joys of His Divinity, is proposed . . . as an object of our tenderest devotion and love; the most attractive, as well as the most fruitful in virtue, that can be offered. In the Adorable Sacrament, this most holy Heart is a fountain of joy, peace, consolation, and grace to all who lovingly approach It in the spirit of faith, humility, and reverence. . . .

"Oh! how much is here for our atoning love!"[54]

It is not strange, therefore, that even before she was a religious, as soon as the chapel in the House of Mercy was completed in May of 1829, Catherine McAuley made immediate plans for the coming Feast of the Sacred Heart to be celebrated with added solemnity. This was twenty-seven years before the feast was extended to the universal Church. On this occasion, too, she formed a group of women into a sodality which had devotion to the Sacred Heart as its object.[55] Later, at George's Hill she would find a like devotedness to encourage and stimulate her. In tracing the spread of the devotion to the Sacred Heart, McGratty[56] credited the Foundress of the Sisters of Mercy with contributing to its nineteenth-century advance.

In Mother McAuley's life the corollary of love for Jesus was love for Mary or, in her own words: "To neglect devotion to Mary is to wound Jesus, because she is His mother."[57] She had put her Institute immediately under Mary's protection by placing it beneath her mantle of Mercy, encouraged unbounded confidence in her intercession, and provided that her feasts be celebrated with joy and devotion. Ordinarily reserved in her choice of words she wrote with particular warmth when referring to devotion to our Blessed Mother: "The Sisters shall always have the warmest and most affectionate devotion to her; regarding her in a special manner as their Mother,"[58] ". . . rejoicing that she has won the Heart of God Himself, so that in her He takes His delight."[59]

The Foundress in turn was inspired by many saints of God who attained holiness in serving God's afflicted for love of Him and who received the necessary strength at the same fountains of grace. There were, to mention but a few, St. Vincent de Paul, St. John of God, St. Camillius of Lellis, and

St. Peter Nolasco, all of whom Mother McAuley named patrons of her Institute.

5. *Capacity for Adaptation*

The essential element which would endure in Mother McAuley's congregation as characterizing her spirit was her mercy toward those in need through love for Christ. This spirit, according to Gallen, lies outside the realm of adaptation. In addition to the purposes common to all religious life, including the striving for evangelical perfection, he lists as constant factors anything essential or fundamental to the Institute and its distinctive, solid spirit. It is true, however, that if this spirit is channeled to society according to the needs of a particular age or culture, the enduring principle will be capable of adaptation in its application. His Holiness, Pope Pius XII, called attention to this fundamental law in his address to superiors general of institutes of religious women on September 15, 1952.

The third criterion applied to test the effectiveness of the work established by Mother McAuley, therefore, was to analyze her personal example of adaptation.

"This demands that we distinguish the essential and immutable from the accidental and changeable in the words and works of the founder and that we do not follow as a rigid norm what the founder did but rather the pliable norm of what he would do in any aspect of life if he were faced by our own age. Furthermore, the founder is not a mere giver of laws but also and primarily a giver of life to his institute. That life is his distinctive spirit, which consists in his approach to the spiritual life, his characteristic virtues, the principles he emphasized, his manner of approaching life and its problems, and the general types of work and zeal that he favored."[61]

Did Mother Catherine in practice have a "pliable norm"

by which her followers may evaluate how she would act if she "were faced by our own age"? Were the means she used rigid or did she adapt them to what best would accomplish the end? And lastly, did she employ the principle of social philosophy which Pope Pius XI expressed so well in his *Quadragesimo Anno* as important to social living: "To help individual members of the social body, but never destroy or absorb them."[62]

Nothing of the portrait drawn of Mother McAuley until now discloses a system of autonomous procedure. That in itself tells a story. There are incidents in her life, nevertheless, which provide more than lip service to such an assumption. She practiced the scriptural wisdom of serpentine adaptability to the contingencies and vagaries of life.

How did Catherine the recent heiress act when, exchanging her life at Coolock House for the company of the underprivileged, she sought from civil authorities permission to enter the public hospitals to visit the sick? Her first step was to obtain permission from her archbishop. She and her companions, while not yet religious, had assumed by this time a simple black costume. Catherine was discerning enough to know that a benevolent secular lady would be successful while a member of a religious society might fail in an undertaking unknown since the so-called Reformation. How did she handle this delicate situation? She began first where she was known. Accompanied by three of her associates she went to Sir Patrick Dun's where her friendship with the senior chief of staff served to give them entry.[63] Through his approval it was possible for the group to be oriented to the hospital and to observe the treatment of the patients. Only after this did Catherine ask whether future visits would be acceptable to the administration. To the other hospitals where she was not known she went in her carriage, and dressed as became her rank in society. This she continued to do until her visits were valued in themselves. When this was achieved she was happy to shed the accessories of which she had availed herself.[64]

Where education was concerned she showed similar good judgment. In its initial stage she displayed her ability to adjust to what was best:

"Thorough in her approach to any problem, Catherine was not content with a study of educational systems employed in Ireland. In the autumn of 1825, accompanied by her close friend, Fanny Tighe,[65] she journeyed to France to investigate educational methods there. We have no record of the impressions she gained but her visit illustrates the alertness of mind and the readiness to profit from the experience of others which was to make her so successful an organizer."[66]

Joined to this was a study of the Kildare Place Society in Dublin, a group that had adopted Joseph Lancaster's system of education established in England. Nano Nagle, however, had introduced the monitorial system of education before Lancaster was born and so Catherine again observed the method in operation at George's Hill. Miley[67] described in detail Catherine McAuley's work as an educator, and Marnane listed her name among others as revealing "by example of their lives, wherein lies the power of the Catholic teacher."[68]

When Mother McAuley's own schools were well established, she continued to encourage and advise the sisters toward self evaluation and improvement. On receiving word that one of the superiors intended utilizing the assistance of the convent in Limerick for this purpose, the Foundress wrote: "If one of your Sisters went there Sister Hartnett,[69] who is exceedingly clever, would teach her in a very short time."[70] But from experience she preferred another method and wrote at some length:

"Would it not be better to try to get a well-qualified Monitress from the Model School until your Sisters would know the method? They sent us such a one from Limerick

. . . I should think they could send you one. She should be paid a small salary out of what the board allows. I do not think they permit any one to attend the Model School in Dublin except those who are settled with them for the purpose and remain all day, paying a certain fee."[71]

Mother McAuley asked the question and gave such information as might be needed in making a wise decision. Nor did she overlook the practical matter of payment for services rendered where others were concerned.

With the establishment of foundations in other cities it became apparent that in addition to schools for the poor there also were needed schools for children of the middle classes. In order to distinguish them from the poor schools these became known as "pension schools." What was the re-action of the Foundress to their inclusion as one of the works of the congregation? Savage wrote:

"Mother McAuley gave her fullest support and encouragement, as she realized that it would be of great value to children whose parents were unable to afford to send them to the more expensive boarding schools. Nor did she consider that such work would prove a distraction from the Sisters' main preoccupation with the poor; on the contrary, she thought that the Sisters could make it serve towards that purpose both by educating the better-off pupils to a sense of their responsibilities towards the poor, and also by providing "nurseries" for suitable vocations to her Institute from which she and her Sisters might hope to win generous associates for their common purpose. . . . In choosing her ministries, Catherine was always guided by local needs and disliked any rigid uniformity."[72]

On one occasion she wrote: "Every place has its own particular ideas and feelings which must be yielded to when possible."[73] And what was the event which brought forth this statement from a religious busily engaged in making foundations to the extent that she remarked that she had used up all her leaders? It was that the poor preferred the ministrations of the professed sisters rather than those of the "net caps" or postulants. In this same letter she stopped to describe the conditions: "The poor here are in a miserable state—the whole surrounding neighborhood one scene of wretchedness and sorrow." To her they were the children of God whose wishes she respected.

The relations of the Foundress with her sisters, whom she had sent to spread her mission of mercy, reveal a like magnanimity of spirit. Without any ado she could send the following answer by mail: "There cannot be any objection to you wearing the cashmere cloaks if you prefer them. I believe the Sisters every where think they have a more religious appearance."[74] It may be discerned that her approach to method was as a means to an end and as such something to be adjusted to the goal in view. Guided by principle in her ordinary actions, the Foundress recognized that there were non-essentials in which more could be accomplished by meeting her neighbor more than halfway.

Reference already has been made to the additional chapters which Mother McAuley wrote in adapting the Presentation Rule for her own Institute. In a chapter of the Presentation Rule which she retained there was one paragraph however which she changed considerably. It dealt with the cheerfulness or joyful reserve by which she wished her followers to be known and which avoided the extremes of strain and levity. In this chapter on "Enclosure" from the Presentation Rule Mother Catherine adapted what she believed would serve her Institute best. She desired a freedom that allowed itself to be consumed joyfully and without display in the service of God. The Archbishop, Dr. Murray, believing that the Mercy Rule would be more quickly approved by Rome if there were few changes from the original Presentation Rule, deleted what the Foundress had written and transposed the original section. Hence this work of Mother McAuley is generally not known.[75] Other illustrations found in her writings bear witness though that she considered a cheerful reserve as characteristic of her Institute: Her retreatents were instructed "to have a cheerful countenance and a manner equally free from constraint or levity."[76] On other occasions she commented on the beauty of such a life by recalling:

"See how quietly the great God performs all His mighty works; darkness is spread over us at night, and light returns in the morning, and there is no noise of closing shutters or drawing curtains. And again: how silently and brilliantly the lamp burns away before the Blessed Sacrament when the oil is pure. It is only when the oil is bad or adulterated that it burns noisily."[77]

It was because her own life burned itself out for God that this valiant religious could attempt all things and adapt herself to diverse situations when principles were not involved. At the very outset of the cholera epidemic she planned a bazaar to raise money for the many families who were being left destitute. Where did she go for aid? To royalty, to her Royal Highness the Duchess of Kent.

"Undaunted by the little prospect, humanly speaking, of enlisting the sympathies of royalty, but rather the certainty of meeting a cold refusal, Reverend Mother, nevertheless, pleaded the cause of the homeless and the destitute, and entreated that her Royal Highness and the Princess Victoria—her present Majesty—would be graciously pleased to give some of their work to be disposed of at the bazaar then in preparation.

"The Duchess returned a most gracious reply, and shortly after a large assortment of fancy work, executed by the royal fingers of mother and daughter, was received at Baggot Street. This valuable contribution was most timely, and a large amount was realized by the princely gifts."[78]

In striking contrast to this queenly incident there is another example in Catherine's life which gives, perhaps, the most convincing evidence of her competency in accommodation. It has been referred to briefly in her biographical sketch. She had built the House of Mercy with ecclesiastical approval, and companions had associated themselves with her work. But while she built, social termites were busily occupied in alienating some on whom she had been accustomed to rely. The Archbishop himself called at Baggot Street in response to her letter. And while he commented that he had authorized no one to inform her that he was considering transferring her establishment to another religious congregation, his manner was cold. He used the occasion to refer to the "title 'Sister of Mercy' which the group had adopted adding that he had not thought of a convent rising up of itself in such a way."[79]

Only a person whose self concept was rooted in God could adapt herself calmly as she did in this circumstance. "Although it pained her naturally, she humbly offered to relinquish the work into the hands of whatever community His Lordship pleased."[80] This was the supreme test of adjustment that God asked of her. In it she saw mirrored God's Will and because her will was in harmony with His she was at peace. But God, through His representative, lifted the cross. And in the time planned by God, He blessed the work she established a thousandfold.

He Himself had chosen her for an apostolic mission in the Church for which He prepared her by bestowing upon her special aptitudes and graces. Catherine McAuley, in turn, cooperated generously in God's plan of mercy for the poor and in caring for the sick to whom she ministered as to Christ. Her spirit will continue to the degree that its worth is prized by nurses, whether religious or lay, who are inspired by her ideals and who walk in her footsteps toward Christ. For the success of her followers lies not in the number of buildings they erect nor in the multiplicity of their activities, but in their ability to discern "the person of their Divine Master" in every person with whom they deal or for whom they labor or pray because in them they "expect to meet their Divine Redeemer." Doing this, His benediction will be theirs. True of each of them, then, will be the words which Mother McAuley applied to another of her own day, and in so doing summarized the story of her own life work:

"This proves to us what the special grace of God can produce though bestowed but on one man, yet so as to go forth amongst millions through the agency of his touch."[81]

PART V

To the Sound of War

WRITTEN into the hearts of men, if not into the pages of all histories of nursing, are important chapters of war nursing by the spiritual daughters of Catherine McAuley. Within thirteen years of her death they nursed the wounded on the battlefields of the Crimean War—a war in which France and England came to Turkey's defense against Russian aggression. Before another decade had spent itself, the Sisters of Mercy in the United States nursed alike the soldiers of the Union and the Confederate armies while their country was torn by civil strife. Forty years later they performed a similar service during the Spanish American War. Since the advent of such organizations as the Red Cross and the Army and Navy nursing services, the sisters for the most part serve their countries in time of war by planning for disaster and rendering nursing care to the civilian population.

The work of the Sisters of Mercy in the Crimea is unknown to many. Others are familiar with only a misrepresented story. For these reasons and because the nursing done on this occasion occurred so nearly within the lifetime of the Foundress and was shared by some trained by her, this chapter of early nursing history of the Sisters of Mercy is apropos.

1. The Call to the Crimea

When war dawned in the spring of 1854, the youth of
Great Britain were quick to join the fleet sailing for the
Black Sea districts; in the autumn of that year shocking
stories reached England's shores of lack of supplies, together
with inadequate medical and nursing care for the wounded.
Henry Edward (later Cardinal) Manning, a friend of Florence Nightingale and Sidney Herbert, with whom he toured
Rome in 1847 while still an Anglican, wrote immediately
to a mutual friend, Mary Stanley: "I have written to the
Bishop of Southwark to see if any Sisters can be found for
the East. Why will not Florence Nightingale give herself
to this great work?"[1]

This Miss Nightingale did, and her offer was accepted
by the War Office. October 24, 1854, found her on her way
to Scutari first by rail and then by sea. Her associates consisted of paid nurses, lady volunteers, and religious. In the
group of ten religious were five Sisters of Mercy under
Mother Mary Clare Moore from Bermondsey, a dockyard
district of London. This quintette had reached Paris on
their way to the Crimea by the time Florence Nightingale
made her appeal for others to accompany her. At the request
of the War Office, the Sisters of Mercy waited there for the
remainder of the party.

Hammack[2] traced in detail from historical sources the
steps which led the government to authorize Bishop Grant
to send these Sisters, and Florence Nightingale's acceptance
to supervise the nursing, and then wrote:

"In view of later developments it seems necessary to
emphasize two points: first, that the five Sisters of Mercy
from Bermondsey had been accepted by the government and
had already left London before Florence Nightingale signed
the contract with the War Office making her superintendent;
and second, that Bishop Grant, after the nuns had already

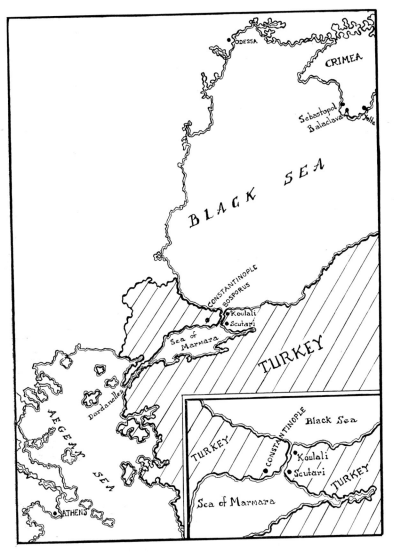

Area surrounding the Black Sea

A ward scene in the Koulali Barrack Hospital, the Koulali General Hospital and the "Hut" Hospital at Balaclava

departed, signed the government contract placing them under Florence Nightingale."[3]

While in Paris the sisters visited the hospitals and "procured several cases of surgical instruments used in military hospitals, which proved a valuable addition to their little stores and a great convenience to the medical officers under whom they worked."[4]

After a trip made eventful by a hurricane, the company reached Malta on October 31 and Constantinople on November 4. The Turkish barracks of Scutari, accommodating five thousand persons and provided by the Sultan for English troops, immediately became the scene of their nursing.

Meanwhile, another group of fifteen sisters from various convents of Mercy in Ireland were answering an appeal sent out from the parenthouse on Baggot Street on October 20, 1854, which read:

"The Government has virtually applied for Sisters, and offered to pay their expenses; and as there is no time to be lost, I beg of you to send your candidates on Tuesday or Wednesday to St. Catherine's."[5]

To the Vicar General, the Very Reverend Dr. Yore, in the absence of the Archbishop, the same superior wrote:

"Attendance on the sick, as you are aware, is part of the work of our Institute, and sad experience amongst the poor has convinced us that, even with the advantage of medical aid, many valuable lives are lost for want of careful nursing."[6]

This correspondence had been initiated by a communication from Sidney Herbert, the Secretary at War, to Bishop Grant authorizing him to seek the aid of additional sisters.[7] Fifteen sisters from a number of convents were selected. Placed as superior for this second group of Sisters of Mercy, and confirmed as such by the War Office, was Mother M. Francis Bridgeman from Kinsale.[8] Less than two months earlier this religious had sent forth from her convent in Kinsale to the city by the Golden Gate the California pioneer band of Sisters of Mercy.

The fifteen sisters became part of the second party of nurses, a unit of forty-eight women, authorized by Sidney Herbert and organized under the leadership of Mary Stanley. The group left London on December second. While in Paris the sisters "placed the mission under the special protection of our Blessed Mother in honor of her Immaculate Conception and procured a Novena of Masses to be offered at Notre Dame de Victoire."[9]

There were the usual perils by sea and beautiful scenes from the ship: Sicily, Athens, and then the Dardanelles. On December 17 the ship anchored at Constantinople. Unaware of what lay before them the company was delighted to see "marble palaces and domes rising out of the placid waters of the Bosphorus into the lovely blue of an Eastern sky."[10] But such joy was fleeting. Before long a message came that they were not wanted at Scutari.

"This sending out of a second band without a formal request from Miss Nightingale was in direct violation of the agreement in the letter which she received from the War Office, in which Sidney Herbert stated that no nurses would be sent out unless she requested them. This letter was printed in *The Times*. Stanmore states that this letter was printed to protect the War Office from requests from private individuals to send out nurses and was not intended to bind the War Office itself. This, however, was not Miss Nightingale's view. The fact remains that Sidney Herbert apparently did not feel himself bound, and in view of the increasing number of patients, and the apparent harmony between Miss Nightingale and the medical staff at Scutari, he saw fit to send reinforcements."[11]

Miss Stanley sought the advice of the British Embassy for her party and was sent temporarily to the summer home of the British Ambassador at Therapia. Mother Bridgeman, "who was always calm in the midst of difficulties, wrote to the Sisters of Charity at Galata, asking hospitality for a short time, till she could see her way as to the future."[12] She and her sisters spent Christmas with the Sisters of Charity and later joined the party at Therapia.

2. *Scutari and Koulali*

Correspondence between Mother Bridgeman and Miss Nightingale, a personal interview arranged by Mother Bridgeman, and finally a conference between Mother M. Clare and herself on the feast of the Epiphany, resulted in five of the sisters leaving Therapia for Scutari on January 8. Mother Bridgeman and four others joined the five English Sisters of Mercy at the General Hospital in Scutari where Miss Nightingale had her headquarters. Among the four was the author of *Memories of the Crimea*. Soon after her arrival Sister M. Aloysius wrote to her superior at St. Leo's, Carlow, in a letter dated January, 1855, and described the conditions at Scutari where cholera raged:

"The hospital consists of long corridors, as far as your eye can reach, with beds at each side; and, as I write, poor fellows, both wounded and frost-bitten, lie on the floor. We are in the wards late and early. When we go to our apartment, to get a couple of hours' rest, we groan in anguish at the thought of all we leave undone."[13]

At the same time Mother Bridgeman and Sister M. Joseph, another of her group, were given nothing to do. After much urging the two were appointed to serve the soup daily, a task which did not take them too long each day. No wonder Mother Bridgeman wrote in her account:

"Oh the misery of that time! to sit in that one room without occupations; without a place to withdraw, even for a few moments, to seek recollection or to ask the aid and light we needed so much. And then to know that we were surrounded by thousands of sufferers whom we had come so far and under such difficuties to serve.

"To know that from fifty to ninety were dying daily, to be sitting idle in the midst of them and to be told by one against whose whim we had no appeal that these needed no nursing care as they were not wounded! To pass daily through these corridors filled with sick and dying fellow creatures, to hear their moans, and to see their crying necessities, and to be debarred by Miss Nightingale from rendering them any of the services we had left our convents to render them: All this, and *much more better untold,* combined to try us in a way one should have felt to appreciate."[14]

Meanwhile during the middle of January a Turkish barrack at Koulali with cavalry stables beneath it was converted into a Barrack Hospital. Lord William Paulett, the Military Commandant at Scutari, was named the medical supervisor of the new undertaking, and Miss Stanley was asked to accept the duty of Lady Superintendent.

"She had originally planned to return to England, as soon as she had turned over her group of nurses to Miss Nightingale, and had remained only to make arrangements for her party. When she realized that unless she accepted the position of Lady Superintendent at Koulali her nurses would remain unemployed, she accepted, and contrary to the wishes of Miss Nightingale, but with the approval of Lord William Paulett, she took the ten nuns from Therapia with her."[15]

During the process of these negotiations Father Ronan, S.J., who had been appointed by the War Office as the chaplain for the Sisters of Mercy, arrived at Scutari. After an interview with Miss Nightingale he drew up a document of which copies were given to both Miss Nightingale and Miss Stanley. In substance the terms were those agreed upon between Dr. Manning and Miss Nightingale before she left London. The paper confirmed Mother Bridgeman as superior of the sisters who had come with her from Ireland; it proposed that ten of the sisters be sent to Koulali, and requested that in addition to the ordinary living quarters there be provided for the sisters, including those from Bermondsey, an oratory for the exercise of their religious obligations. The sisters were to have full liberty in attending to the spiritual needs of Roman Catholics and at the same time pledged themselves not to interfere with the religious concerns of Protestants.[16]

Mother Bridgeman, after appointing one to be responsible for the five sisters she had left at Scutari, was among the ten who went to Koulali arriving there on January 27, 1855. Within a week a second hospital, the General Hospital, was opened. Five of the Sisters of Mercy worked at the Barrack Hospital during the day; the other five nursed at the General Hospital where the ten sisters were housed from its opening on February 2. "Miss Stanley, unable to supervise both hospitals, named Reverend Mother Bridgeman as Superintendent, although she nominally remained in charge of both hospitals."[17]

The story of how the nursing care and management of the hospitals at Scutari and Koulali differed in the extreme is evident throughout a book written by an eyewitness, *Eastern Hospitals and English Nurses,* a story of the Crimea by a Lady Volunteer. Fanny Taylor, the author, wrote at length of the work of Mother Bridgeman and the Sisters of Mercy. A few selections suffice to indicate the satisfaction given and the spirit which prevailed:

"The mother had four sisters, two ladies, and two nurses,

to assist her. She had had a long experience in hospital work, and possessed a skill and judgment in nursing attained by few. The hospital, from first to last, was admirably managed. The medical officers, both Dr. Hamilton and Dr. Guy, and the assistant-surgeons, fully appreciated her value, and there was a hearty cooperation between them. When the means of improvement were placed in her hands they were judiciously used, and the hospital so improved that it became the admiration of all who visited it, and the pride of the ladies and nurses who worked in it; we used to call it 'the model hospital of the East.' "[18]

On the next page, the author continues:

"Visitors to the General Hospital usually visited the sisters, for they were universally beloved and respected, and they received all who called upon them with the utmost courtesy and sweetness of manner.

"Their community room was a tolerably-sized and pleasant one, and furnished with the utmost simplicity . . . and the warm welcome we ever met there, made it a pleasant resting-place after ascending the steep hill from the Barrack Hospital.

"Few of us had ever visited nuns before, and we often remarked among ourselves the bright, joyous spirit which pervaded the sisters one and all; in their work evidently consisted their happiness, and we often marvelled also at their untiring industry. They never seemed to pass an idle moment, for in their leisure time they were always busy about some needlework or drawing."[19]

Was it during these happy visits that Mother Bridgeman's thought turned to her sisters leaving Kinsale for a mission in far-off San Francisco? Or was it mere coincidence that the author, in writing of the spread of the community to various parts of the world singled out for special mention California as well as America?

Miss Stanley arranged to return to England at Easter time. Her methods at Koulali had never received approval from Miss Nightingale who, while nominally in charge of the nursing, never visited the Koulali hospitals. Earlier she had conveyed to Sidney Herbert the possibility of resigning this charge, to which he replied in a letter dated March 5, 1855. He told her that his successor, Lord Panmure, wished "to separate the different hospitals, as far as nursing is concerned," because the "multiplication of hospitals at some miles' distance makes any real supervision from Scutari impossible, and gives you, therefore, a responsibility without corresponding powers." He adds his own impressions by saying that such an arrangement "would leave you unfettered, and with undiminished powers in the two principal hospitals which have been the theatre of your exertions, and in which you are so much interested. What is more, I feel certain that it will be by far the best arrangement for you. . . . You will, therefore, carry on your own system at the two hospitals at Scutari, supported by Dr. Cumming."[20]

Among a new group of ladies who had arrived from England was a Miss Hutton whom Lord Paulett chose to succeed Miss Stanley. There were now thirty-two ladies and nurses at Koulali in addition to the ten sisters. In accordance with the wishes of Miss Hutton and with Lord Paulett's approval Mother Bridgeman continued, as before, the responsibility of the General Hospital.

The summer of 1855 was a pleasant one and the work began to decrease. Yet during these months the sisters experienced a petty persecution which must be read in its entirety to be appreciated. At last Lord Paulett had to admit "that he never knew of one fair case against the Sisters. That he had never heard any but the most favorable accounts of their nursing."[21] He promised, moreover, that as long as they fulfilled their contract he would take care that they would not be troubled.[22] The new purveyor-in-chief, Mr. Robert-son, described by Mother Bridgeman as "a Protestant and a Scotchman—one of the most truly kind and liberal minded men I ever met,"[23] did all in his power to make their work-ing and living conditions more suitable. Their dormitory was partitioned so that they now could have a small oratory where for the first time the Blessed Sacrament was reserved.

During this interval Miss Nightingale was at Balaclava where she had gone in May. But while touring the hospitals there she was stricken by a fever which made it necessary for her to be returned to Scutari.[24] She wrote a letter from there on July 5 to Sister M. Elizabeth indicating her dis-pleasure with the new arrangements and reminding her that it was only with her assent that the English government had permitted Catholic nuns to come to the scenes of battle. She apparently had forgotten that the Sisters of Mercy left Eng-land two days before Miss Nightingale had been named to superintend the nursing in the Crimea.[25]

By September the patients in the hospitals at Koulali were few in number and not acutely ill. Plans were in prog-ress to return the buildings to the Turks who were in need of them. While Mother Bridgeman was considering where her sisters might be of service, Sir John Hall, inspector-general of all the Crimean hospitals, was notified by Miss Nightingale that she was withdrawing her nurses and resign-ing the charge of the Crimean hospital at Balaclava on Octo-ber first. The fall of Sebastopol was effected on September 8 and the Crimea, pending peace negotiations, became head-quarters for the army of occupation. Dr. Hall was happy, therefore, to hear from Father Woolett, S.J., the Catholic chaplain at the Crimean camp, that on Miss Nightingale's withdrawal the Sisters of Mercy were willing to come to the General Hospital at Balaclava. They had passed from Miss Nightingale's control when she resigned the charge of the Koulali hospitals. The five who were under her superintend-ence because of their presence at Scutari were not removed by Mother Bridgeman until she wrote to Miss Nightingale requesting that they be allowed to join her. Moreover, Mother Bridgeman had in her possession a letter from Sidney Herbert directing her to find work wherever she could, or to feel free to return home.[26]

3. Balaclava

The travelers crossed the Black Sea and reached Balaclava on October 10. Miss Nightingale accompanied the group, bringing with her the Irish sisters who had worked with her at Scutari, and remained for several weeks. On their second day Sir John Hall visited the sisters to welcome them and constitute Mother Bridgeman as superintendent of the General Hospital.

The hospital consisted of a main building of stone construction and some twelve or more wooden huts on a hill. Of these one was reserved for the use of the sisters, the others were for patients. Each sister had charge of two wards and had some orderlies to help her. There were no secular volunteers or nurses. The deep mud in which the sisters walked from hut to hut was small discomfort in comparison with the droves of rats which were their unfailing companions working or sleeping.

Before the first week had passed a severe cholera epidemic reached Balaclava. Victims of this disease had been nursed at both Scutari and Koulali, and God had spared the sisters. Now Sister M. Winifred was struck and succumbed in a day. Several hundred patients died the first week. The sisters nursed the sick both day and night, carrying out the chloroform treatment then in use which required constant attention.

With the dawn of 1856, fevered typhus patients continued to demand constant care. Sister M. Aloysius described the importance of the night nursing, and the giving of nourishment every two hours or more frequently as required, adding that "the doctors were often surprised in the morning to find their patients so well over the night—no matter how clever a doctor may be, if he has not a good nurse, who will attend strictly to his directions, little can be done."[27] This coincides with a report sent later to the War Office by Mr. David Fitzgerald, the Deputy-Purveyor:

"The superiority of an ordered system is beautifully illustrated in the Sisters of Mercy. One mind appears to move all and their intelligence, delicacy, and conscientiousness invest them with a halo of confidence extreme. The medical officer can safely consign his most critical case to their hands. Stimulants or opiates ordered every five minutes will be faithfully administered tho' the five minutes' labour were repeated uninterruptedly for a week.

"The number of Sisters, without being large, is sufficient to secure for every patient needing it their share of attention."[28]

On the twenty-third of February typhus claimed the life of Sister M. Elizabeth. She was laid to rest at the side of Sister M. Winifred on the rugged hill overlooking the Black Sea. The soldiers marked the graves with white marble crosses, planted flowers and evergreens, and enclosed the plot by a high iron railing set in cut stone.[29]

But there were sorrows to be endured which cut more deeply than the loss of loved companions. Despite the satisfaction of the medical officers with the nursing care given to the patients, rumors again were circulated that proselytism was the sisters' concern. At the same time it was said that they gave greater attention to the Catholic patients. To investigate these charges, Dr. Hall corresponded with doctors and Protestant ministers who had observed the work of the sisters at Koulali. The answers he received assured him that Mother Bridgeman and her sisters were the victims of bigotry. "However, he kept the letters on file in case of future investigations by the War Office."[30] Later, they were published in Mitra's biography of Hall.

As before, these trials of the sisters were matched by those in charge of Balaclava by doing what was in their power to make the work easier and by maintaining cordial relationships. Two new huts were built to be occupied by the sisters, and the walk through mud, snow, and ice from hut to main hospital was eliminated by building a simple flight of stairs.

The cold war against the sisters continued, resulting in an inspection of the hospital and detailed reports. Notwithstanding Miss Nightingale's strong urging that the number of sisters at Balaclava be reduced, Colonel Lefroy's report did not press this issue. Miss Hutton had returned to England and from there wrote as a true friend: "Dear Mother how little do the malice and evil speaking of some, and the misjudgment of others matter when set against the real good accomplished. . . . I will not have *my* Rev'd. Mother and Sisters misrepresented."[31] Emily Hutton was true to her word. To Cardinal Wiseman she wrote on February 7:

"Of the labors of the Sisters of Mercy in the Crimea it is not for me to speak. I know of them only by report of those who *witness* them and thankfully bear testimony to their priceless value, but of the twelve nuns now working at Balaclava eight were under my direction at Kulalee from the 10th of April to Oct. 1st 1855. I consider it a privilege to bear witness to their devotion and obedience, to the perfect truthfulness and exquisite tact with which they performed the duties of nurses during these weary months.

"As an individual my testimony is of little value, but the position which I occupied gave me opportunity which no other possessed of watching, and I did so narrowly, the spirit which guided them and the manner in which their work was done. Rather than [that] the deep injustice of refusing all honor and thanks to the Roman Catholic Sisters of Mercy should be done, in England's name, I have broken the silence most dear and most fitting to a woman.

"Much more might be said, but I know that neither the Mother Francis nor her Sisters seek for praise here and at the risk of exciting a smile at Protestant fondness for Scriptural allusion I would add, that they are surely Blessed in not receiving their reward of men."[32]

With the coming of March came renewed hope that peace would be declared, and thoughts turned toward home. Yet before this was to be realized another crisis was to be faced. It was the order for which Florence Nightingale had been working and waiting. Dated March 16, 1856, and issued from Sebastopol, it read:

"It is notified by desire of the Secretary of War that Miss Nightingale be recognized by her Majesty's Government as the General Superintendent of the female nursing establishment in the military hospitals of the Army.

"No lady or Sister, or nurse is to be transferred from one hospital nor introduced into any hospital without previous consultation with her.

"Her instructions however require her to have the approval of the Principal Medical Officer in her exercise of the responsibility thus vested in her.

"The Principal Medical Officer will communicate with Miss Nightingale upon all subjects connected with the female nursing establishment and will give instructions thro' that lady.

> By order (signed)
> C. A. Windham
> Chief of the Staff"[33]

This promulgation followed and was incorporated as part of the letter from Lord Panmure to General Sir William J. Codrington bearing the heading: War Department, February 25th, 1856.[34]

Florence Nightingale arrived in Balaclava on March 25, 1856. That day she held two interviews with Mother Bridgeman and refused to accept the latter's decision not to renew connections which had existed and been broken by Miss

Nightingale on the sisters' arrival. Mother Bridgeman then referred her to Dr. Hall. Ensuing correspondence testified to his personal preference. On March 26 he wrote in part to Miss Nightingale:

"In justice to [Mrs. Bridgeman] and the Sisters under her orders I must state that they have given me the most perfect satisfaction by the quiet and efficient manner in which they have performed their duty since they have been employed there, and I should regret their departure."[35]

4. The Return Home

On March 28 Mother Bridgeman submitted her resignation to Dr. Hall in writing. Hardly had she done this when Miss Nightingale again visited her in an attempt to make her change her mind. That Mother Bridgeman could act with grace under stress is evident from the outcome of the interview. She yielded to the urging to take a week in which to reconsider the matter and wrote to Dr. Hall:

"In the meantime matters are to stay as they are. Though I believe it is not at all likely I shall change in a week the *fixed resolve of months,* I thought it better to consent to this and suspend any movement until the time named, as no violation of principle is involved."[36]

Following the period for reconsideration another conference was held. In this interview Miss Nightingale stated clearly that while she would not interfere with the spiritual duties of the sisters, the same would not be true in regard to hospital arrangements. Undoubtedly, Mother Bridgeman's experiences with her over a period of approximately fifteen months were convincing evidence that nothing which she or her sisters might do would meet with Miss Nightingale's satisfaction. When hundreds and thousands of men were in

need of nursing, this care would be given without the hope
of human recognition and in the face of prejudice and mis-
interpretation. But now few patients remained and before
long the hospital would be closed. The decision was to return home.

Once it became clear to Miss Nightingale that this decision was final she requested from Mother Bridgeman an
account of the sisters' manner of nursing. In the hope that
someone would profit, Mother Bridgeman explained the
method while Miss Nightingale took notes.[37]

Peace had been declared on March 30, 1856. While this
was not known immediately in Balaclava, the glad tidings
had reached the Crimea a week before Mother Bridgeman
and her sisters left for home. During these last days two letters of commendation came to them: The first one dated
April 5, 1856, read:

"I cannot permit you, and the Sisters under your direction to leave the Crimea without an expression of the high
opinion I entertain of your ministration, and of the very
important aid you have rendered to the sick under your care.

"I can most conscientiously assert, as I have on other
occasions stated, that you have given me the most perfect
satisfaction ever since you assumed charge of the nursing
department in the general hospital at Balaklava, and I do
most unfeignedly regret your departure, but after what has
occurred, I would not, even with that feeling uppermost in
my mind, urge you to stay.

"I enclose a letter from Sir William Codrington, Commander in Chief, expressive of the sense he entertains of
your services, and of those of the Sisters under you, which
I trust will be acceptable to your feelings; and I feel assured
you must leave us with an approving conscience, as I know
you do with the blessing of all those whom you have aided
in their hour of need.

"To Him who sees all our outward actions, and knows

our inmost thoughts and wishes, I commend you. And may He have you, and those under you, in His holy keeping is the prayer of

Yours faithfully
John Hall
Inspector Gen. of Hospitals"[38]

The other, dated April 6, 1856, and sent to Dr. Hall read:

"I regret much to hear that circumstances have induced Mrs. Bridgeman, the Mother Superioress of the Roman Catholic nurses, to quit the General Hospital, and proceed to England with the nurses who have been so long associated with her.

"I request you to assure that lady of the high estimation in which her services and those of her nurses are held by us all; founded as that opinion is upon the experience of yourself, the medical officer of the hospital, and of the many patients, both wounded and sick, who, during 14 or 15 months past, have benefited by their care.

"I am quite sure that their unfailing kindness will have the reward which Mrs. Bridgeman values, viz., the remembrance and gratitude of those who have been the object of such distinterested attention.

Your obedient servant
W. Codrington
General Commander"[39]

The sisters set sail on the eleventh of April and arrived in London on the sixth of May. Their reception has been set to verse in "Tilbury Dock." (See Appendix D) Some of them soon after left for the parenthouse in Dublin, which they reached on the Feast of Corpus Christi. A royal welcome awaited them and a *Te Deum* was sung.

So ended the story of the second band of sisters who left for the Crimea. The Bermondsey group remained for several more months and reached England on July 27. Mother M. Clare, however, had been forced to return home on April 28 because of ill health. Florence Nightingale always remained on friendly terms with her. In a farewell letter addressed the day after the departure, and which awaited Mother M. Clare at Bermondsey on her arrival May 16, Miss Nightingale wrote:

"My dearest Reverend Mother:

"Your going home is the greatest blow I have yet had, but God's blessing and my love and gratitude go with you, as you well know. You know well, too, that I shall do everything I can for the Sisters whom you have left me. But it will not be like you. Your wishes will be our law. And I shall try and remain in the Crimea for their sakes as long as we are any of us there. I do not presume to express praise or gratitude to you, reverend mother, because it would look as if I thought you had done the work, not unto God, but unto me. I will ask you to forgive me for everything and anything I may have done which could ever have given you pain, remembering only that I have always felt that it has given me more pain to reign over you than you to serve. You were far above me in fitness for the General Superintendency, both in worldly talent of administration, and far more in the spiritual qualifications which God values in a Superior. The being placed over you in our inenviable reign in the East was my misfortune and not my fault. I trust you will not withdraw any of the Sisters now here till the work of the hospitals ceases to require their presence, and that I may be authorized to judge of this.

"Dearest reverend mother, what you have done for the work no one can ever say. But God will reward you for it with Himself. If I thought that your valuable health would be restored by a return home I should not regret it. But I feel that unless you give up work for a time . . . your return to Bermondsey will only be a signal for greater calls upon your strength. However, it matters little, provided we spend our lives to God, whether like our Blessed Lord's, they are concluded in three-and-thirty years or whether they are prolonged to old age.

"My love and gratitude will be yours, dearest reverend mother, wherever you go. I do not presume to give you any tribute but my tears; and as I shall soon want a 'character' from you, as my respected Sister M. Gonzaga would say, I am not going to give you a character. But I should be glad that the Bishop of Southwark should know, and Dr. Manning (though my recommendation is not likely to be of value to you, but the contrary), that you were valued as you deserve, and that the gratitude of the army is yours. And believe me, dearest reverend mother, ever gratefully, lovingly, overflowingly yours,

Florence Nightingale."[40]

Such a response from Miss Nightingale speaks well for Mother M. Clare and the lessons she learned from the Foundress, Mother M. Catherine McAuley, in the early days at Baggot Street. For the great war nurse did not bestow praise lightly. Stanmore, in writing the life of Sidney Herbert, said of Miss Nightingale:

"I look in vain for praise or approval of any individual, except herself, Mr. and Mrs. Bracebridge, and two doctors. Every one else, high and low, male and female, Lord Stratford, Lord Raglan, Lady Stratford, Miss Stanley, and all Miss Stanley's companions, Lord William Paulet, Dr. Smith, Dr. Hall, Dr. Cumming, Dr. Menzies, Mr. Filder, Mr. Wreford, and hosts of inferior officers and others, including all her own staff 'except about 16,' are denounced with the utmost vigour of expression, not merely as inefficient but as utterly incompetent and incapable. She indeed went so far as to say—and that more than once—that she herself and five others (the Bracebridges and doctors aforesaid) were the only people who cared at all for the sick, or had done anything for their relief."[41]

The association of the sisters with a personality which showed "a jealous impatience of any rival authority,"[42] plus the period in England's history in which the sisters nursed the wounded of the Crimean battlefields accounts for their uneventful return. Indeed, as the editor of the Crimean Diary notes so well, Mother M. Francis Bridgeman

"lived in Ireland during the time of the repeal of the last penal law against the Catholics. Also, that the repeal of such laws did not necessarily mean that England changed her way of thinking, or that nuns could rise high in her service without causing bitter enmity within the ranks."[43]

To the Turkish Sultan, on the other hand, such prejudice was unknown. He knew only that the sisters had nursed the Turks as well as the Christians in the Ottoman Empire. Hence, before the year 1856 had drawn to a close Bishop Grant received word that the Sultan of Constantinople wished to bestow a mark of appreciation on the sisters. The gift was 230 pounds. The offer of money proposed a problem since the sisters' services had been solely from a motive of charity. They were gratified with the assurance that this was not to be construed as remuneration. Rather, they could consider it as money for the poor and infirm, of which they were to be the dispensers. The money was divided amongst the eight convents according to the number of sisters represented in the Crimea from where it was distributed to the poor and sick.[44]

Leslie has said of the work of the sisters in the Crimea:

"Unexpectedly they came to the Crimea, and suddenly they returned. When the war was over they took up their slight belongings and were gone—so swiftly and silently that no historian recorded their names, no assembly offered them eulogy, and no ruler sent them decorations. They were quite forgotten, which was perhaps what they desired."[45]

Forgotten, yes, for forty years. Then in 1897 Queen Victoria, who had ascended the throne of England in the lifetime of the Foundress, celebrated the Diamond Jubilee of her reign. Part of the Jubilee ceremonies included bestowing the Royal Red Cross upon the sisters who had gone to the Crimea.[46] Five survived: four in England and one in Ireland.

Sister M. Aloysius from County Galway had just written her Crimean Memoirs. When word was received that she was to be decorated she begged leave not to appear in person because "the weight of seventy-six years and the infirmities of age" were upon her. She accepted the honor "in recognition of the services of my Sisters in religion and my own in caring for the wounded soldiers at the Crimea during the war."[47]

The Sisters of Mercy in London were able to go to Windsor and be decorated in person by Queen Victoria. It was a Friday and the sisters were touched to see that fish had been prepared for their lunch. But more than forty years in religion did not serve to elicit like emotions to the sudden attendance by two footmen! The more timid were dismayed; others took it in stride and were thrilled. All were charmed with the kindness and simplicity of the Queen, and her gay laughter to the inquiry of one of them: "Would it be in order for me to kiss your hand please ma'am?"[48]

During all these years Florence Nightingale's friendship with the sisters from Bermondsey continued. To Mother M. Stanislaus, the last Crimean veteran of the Sisters of Mercy and who survived her by three years, Miss Nightingale wrote toward the end of 1886:

"10 South St. Park Lane W.

Dec. 30/86

"My dear Sister Stanislaus
"May I send you all Christmas good wishes and hearty prayers for the Almighty Father's best New Year's blessings for you and yours in the form of a picture?

"Pray for me that the Child Jesus may be born in my heart.

"How long it is since I have heard from you. But Christmas evergreens have carried to you a little bit of my heart every year.

"Life is too busy for both of us to look back upon the Crimea much. But when I think of it I always look back upon you, dearest Sister, in the little General Hospital at Balaclava.

"And dear, dear Rev'd Mother at Scutari now a saint in Heaven.

"May I send you a little contribution for your work? Tell me a little about it. My love to any of the Sisters whom I know whom you still have with you.

"God bless & prosper you all & your work. Fare you very well.

Ever yours, tho' in silence yet in heart
F. Nightingale

"Did you ever tell me whether I should send back any of the books dear Rev'd Mother lent or gave me—which I so valued?

FN"[49]

Mother M. Stanislaus died in 1913, almost sixty years after she answered her country's call to nurse the wounded of the battlefield. Her body was escorted from the church to the cemetery by a bearer party of the Royal Army Medical Corps provided by the War Office. It was a mark of appreciation of her work both during and after the Crimean War. On her return from Scutari she had been one of the founders of St. Elizabeth's Hospital in London.[50] At her death her sisters in religion were well known for their hospital work throughout the world.

Mercy Hospital, Pittsburgh, Pennsylvania—1847
Pioneer hospital of the Sisters of Mercy

Mercy Hospital, Chicago, Illinois—1851
Second hospital of the Sisters of Mercy

St. Mary's Hospital, San Francisco, California—1855
Third "Mercy" hospital in the U.S. and one of first six hospitals of
Sisters of Mercy in the United States, Ireland, and England

The Mater Misericordiae Hospital, Dublin
Plans begun in 1852; foundation stone laid in 1856;
dedicated in 1861.

Hospital of St. John and St. Elizabeth
London—1856
Requested of Mother M. Clare Moore
on her return to London from
Crimean battlefields.

Jervis Street Hospital, Dublin
Founded in 1718; operated by the
Sisters of Mercy since 1854

PART VI

ACCORDING TO THE PATTERN

FOLLOWING the death of Mother Mary Catherine McAuley an interlude of five years was marked by the establishment of new foundations. In the first year three sisters went to Newfoundland. Prior to the second anniversary seven sisters, under the leadership of Mother M. Francis Warde, left Ireland to establish the first Convent of Mercy in the United States, and arrived in Pittsburgh on December 21, 1843. Little time was lost wherever the sisters went in extending the spirit of mercy to the care of the sick. Then came the decade in which were launched the first in the chain of hospitals conducted by Mother McAuley's spiritual daughters and which today encircle the globe.

1. A Decade of Years

New Years' Day, 1847, marks the beginning of Mercy's many hospitals. For on this day in the city of Pittsburgh an institution named Mercy Hospital opened its doors to the public. It was an unoccupied section of an old hotel called Concert Hall in which the sisters resided. It was truly a "first" even beyond that of its own religious congregation. It claims the distinction of being the first hospital in Western Pennsylvania and "the first Catholic hospital, still extant, to be erected in the eastern states."[1]

The presence of typhus or what was then known as "ship fever" within the next year and a half resulted in the converted concert hall being used as an emergency hospital and the erection of a new Mercy Hospital on the location which it still occupies. Before this change was made however three sisters within the matter of a week paid the price of caring for the "contagious patients" with their lives.

Before the sisters in Pittsburgh had achieved the goal of a hospital of their own in which to minister to the needs of the sick in their city, six sisters, with Mother M. Agatha O'Brien as superior, were sent westward to gain other souls to Christ. They reached Chicago on the eve of the Feast of Our Lady of Mercy, 1846, and immediately engaged in teaching and social welfare work.

Mercy Hospital, Chicago, had its origin on February 27, 1851. A year earlier some doctors had utilized space in Lake House, a flourishing hotel situated on the lake shore, styling the establishment the Illinois General Hospital. To save the venture these men turned to the sisters. The Sisters of Mercy in turn doubled the capacity to twenty-four beds and changed the name. Within several years a new building and a new site became a necessity. The year 1869 witnessed the erection of the Mercy Hospital which has served Chicago long and faithfully.[2]

Threads fashioning the shadow of the cross characterize the mosaic of the early work of the Sisters of Mercy in this city. In 1854 Chicago was visited by an epidemic of Asiatic cholera. The sisters generously nursed the sick and dying in their homes. Within one twenty-four-hour period Mother M. Agatha and three of her companions succumbed to the disease and answered their final call.[3] This was but one of many trials of the early pioneers. Nevertheless, Mercy Hospital appears to have been singularly blessed. It escaped the Chicago fire of 1871 and cared for the injured of the conflagration; its name is linked with the renowned surgeon of early American medicine, Dr. J. P. Murphy; and its growth is one with the Midwestern city which arose from an expanse of prairie along Lake Michigan.

At the parent house in Dublin preparations also were in progress to forward the hopes of the Foundress to nurse the sick in hospitals conducted by the sisters. For this purpose several sisters were sent to Europe in 1852 to become familiar with the systems of a number of noted hospitals there, particularly Amiens in France.[4] Meanwhile, Mother M. Vincent Whitty had completed arrangements for building the Mater Misericordiae Hospital,[5] but the foundation stone was not placed until June 1, 1856.

The guiding spirit behind this great undertaking was Mother M. C. Xavier Maguire who proceeded on the principle that the work of those who labor for God's glory should at least equal if not excel that of the many who toil only for an earthly reward. Only when poverty was relieved in the spirit dictated by the Gospel did it deserve the name of charity. Archbishop Paul (later Cardinal) Cullen in speaking at the solemn opening of this four-hundred bed hospital on the feast of Our Lady of Mercy, 1861, could say: "The Sisters of Mercy [acting according to the spirit of their Institute], determined to adopt the plan best calculated to elevate and ennoble poverty, and they have been most successful in erecting a hospital which does credit to their good taste and is a great ornament to the city."[6]

Today advisory councils are emphasized as being essential to the good management of hospitals. In 1867 the Mater Misericordiae Hospital published a report covering the years from 1855. The records at this time reveal that the sisters had "called to their aid a committee or council of the leading gentlemen of Dublin, to whom the accounts are thrown open, and whose advice and cooperation are gratefully received."[7] During these years the sisters were the only nurses in the hospital. Theirs was a "ministry of gentle hearts and delicate hands in smoothing the poor man's pillow, cheering him in his depression, and lightening his pain."[8]

The administration of one of Dublin's oldest hospitals, the Charity Infirmary on Jervis Street, was taken over by the Sisters of Mercy in 1854. It was here some twenty years earlier that Dr. Corrigan, with only six of the seventy beds reserved for medical patients, established his sound diagnostic techniques in cardiac conditions.⁹ Was he among the deputation who received Mother Whitty and her three companions on the fifteenth of August, 1854? This would be interesting information to be sure, but of less importance than knowledge of the quality of nursing care given by the sisters. Reference to the latter has been made in this manner:

> "The Jervis Street Hospital, founded by six surgeons in 1718, was to become a century and a half later, the scene of the revival of skilled nursing at the hands of the Sisters of Mercy."¹⁰

The sisters have continued to the present at the Jervis Street Hospital and in the intervening years have increased the capacity to 242 beds and have added an outpatient department.

These two Dublin hospitals of the Sisters of Mercy have become associated with the name of Matt Talbot, the alcoholic who became a Christian hero. For it was at the Mater Hospital that his cardiac condition was diagnosed, where he received treatment during the last two years of his life, and where he was anointed during his last hospitalization. When he dropped dead in Granby Lane on his way to a second Mass on Trinity Sunday, June 7, 1925, an ambulance rushed him to the Jervis Street Hospital. There he was pronounced dead and his body was prepared for burial by an orderly and a nurse assisted by Sister M. Ignatius.

In the same year that the sisters went to Jervis Street, a foundation of sisters left Kinsale, County Cork, for San Francisco. Mother M. Baptist Russell and seven sisters, sailed through the Golden Gate and disembarked on December 8, 1854. The superior's decision "that visitation of the sick and poor in their wretched homes would be the best way to launch the mission of Mercy"¹¹ was timely indeed. For in less than a year after the sisters' arrival, Asiatic cholera was brought to the port city and assumed epidemic proportions.

Gold rush settlers lacked the basic knowledge needed to care for those stricken with the plague.

"To the distressed city Mother Russell immediately offered the nursing services of the Sisters, whose experience in the 1849 cholera epidemic in Ireland was invaluable. The generous offer was seized upon, and for six weeks Mother Russell's Sisters gave twenty-four hour service, night and day shifts going in rotation to the public hospital to work among the stricken."[12]

When the epidemic was over the city managers, fortified with firsthand experience of the sisters' nursing ability, asked Mother Baptist Russell to assume charge of the indigent sick. It was in this way that the St. Mary's Hospital of today had its unique beginning on October 24, 1855. Unique, because Mother Russell purchased for this purpose with borrowed money the State Marine Hospital which happened to be for sale, and was to receive from the city Board of Supervisors $400 a month in the form of rent.

It is significant that the bigotry which caused her former superior, Mother M. Francis Bridgeman, such suffering in the Crimea had its counterpart in the Know Nothing movement which simultaneously attacked Mother Russell and the work of her sisters during this first year. These were San Francisco's Vigilante Days of 1856. In addition to this, the sisters were to learn in the school of experience that the financial obligations assumed under contract by the city were never to be met. In March, 1857, the Board of Supervisors were reminded that the sisters could not continue caring for 150 to 170 patients without some remuneration and on July 19 the last county patient was transferred to a municipal hospital in North Beach.

The old brick building on Stockton Street, serving first as the American Hotel, the Kremlin, and the Clarendon Hotel, then as the State Marine Hospital, and finally in name at least as the San Francisco City and County Hospital, had placed over its doors on July 27, 1857, the name of St. Mary's Hospital. Mother Russell had believed in 1855 that she was operating a public institution; by 1857 there was no doubt that it was a private hospital instead. Without in a sense being aware of it she had established almost two years earlier the first Catholic Hospital on the Pacific Coast of the United States.[13]

Mother Russell had looked to the future and a new St. Mary's by buying a lot overlooking South Beach prior to May, 1857. The cornerstone for this hospital on Rincon Hill at the corner of First and Bryant Streets was laid in 1861 and the patients were transferred several months later. The first half-century of St. Mary's, like that of its sister Mercy Hospitals, was filled with lights and shadows.

The nursing of the smallpox victims in the epidemic of 1868 resulted in the city granting to the sisters free transportation on the municipal streetcars. This privilege the members of all religious communities of women in San Francisco still enjoy. The year 1906 brought San Francisco its memorable earthquake in the early morning of April 18. St. Mary's had suffered no damage but the major fires rapidly breaking out all over the city made evacuation of the 170 patients an immediate necessity. A Sacramento river boat, *The Modoc,* was secured. No sooner had it pushed away from its mooring, at five in the evening with its patients and staff, when the flames could be seen leaping from the hospital windows.[14] A building on Sutter Street served temporary purposes until the St. Mary's of today was completed in 1911.

It will be recalled that St. Mary's foundation coincided with the labors of the Sisters of Mercy in the Crimean war. On Mother M. Clare Moore's return to London in the spring of 1856 a request from Cardinal Wiseman awaited her to staff an institution for the care of the sick. In that same year on November 18, the Feast of St. Elizabeth of Hungary, she installed Mother M. Gonzaga and three other sisters at the Hospital for Incurables on Great Ormand Street. The institution was named St. Elizabeth's Hospital. It was England's first post-Reformation Catholic hospital.

By June 24 of the following year the hospital had been remodeled and enlarged and there were fifty patients, about twenty of whom were children. All were charity patients since admission was reserved to these. The name was changed to the Hospital of St. John and St. Elizabeth because of the close association with the Order of St. John of Jerusalem, a member of which built the convent and chapel, and pledged further contributions to the hospital. This Order has membership on the present Board of Management.

Some of the notations made a century ago make interesting reading today:

"Each ward has a book-case. The children have hobbyhorses and toys enough to fit up a store. . . . There is a sliding door through which the patients hear Mass and even sermons. [These were the days before intercommunication!] From the third ward they can look into the sanctuary. It is a real home for the poor. . . . Only incurables are received but many get well owing to the excellent nursing they receive."[15]

The hospital was transferred to St. John's Wood in 1898. Two years later the present buildings were formally opened. This is a voluntary hospital exempt from state control, where the poor continue to be treated free of charge and where "those patients who are able to do so are asked to make a contribution towards the cost of maintenance, but no means test is taken."[16]

These six hospitals of the Sisters of Mercy referred to above, three in the United States, two in Ireland, and one in England, had their origin within fifteen years after

Mother McAuley's life came to an end. Each has kept pace with changes in medicine and nursing service while giving care to suffering humanity in Christ's name for a century or more.

2. Down the Days of Many Years

a. Hospitals

In the next three decades and a half (1856-91) which rounded out the first half-century of the Congregation's existence without the guiding hand of its Foundress, other hospitals and the first schools of nursing came into being. Some of these hospitals are no longer in existence; of those which remain until the present the first of this period was the Mercy Hospital in Cork, Ireland, founded in 1857. In the north of Ireland the Mater Infirmary hospital opened its doors in 1883.

In the United States nineteen hospitals still in operation had their origin between 1856 and 1891.

These and their three predecessors continue to do a gigantic task in hospital administration today. A comparison of the one-hundred-thirty-one institutions of the Sisters of Mercy in the United States for the care of sick humanity with these pioneering twenty-two is revealing. While they represent but 17 per cent of the total, in 1956 they provided 28 per cent of the beds and bassinets and had 25 per cent of the admissions and births.

The majority of the hospitals conducted by the Sisters of Mercy in various parts of the world are found in the United States. They are represented in 63 per cent of the states, and in the state of Iowa alone the sisters have twenty institutions. The 1956 United States figures may be summarized as follows:[17]

General hospitals 110
Special hospitals 21

    General and Nervous and Mental Conditions 1⎫
    Nervous and Mental Conditions .... 5⎰ 6
    Tuberculosis 1
    Maternity, or Pediatrics and Maternity 2
    Convalescent, Chronic, or Aged Chronic 12

CAPACITY Beds and Bassinets

Size	Number	Percent
Under 99	42	32
100 to 199	40	30
200 to 299	22	17
300 to 399	18	14
400 to 750	9	7

TOTAL Beds and Admissions

	Subtotal	Total
Beds	20,504⎫	
Bassinets	3,357⎰	23,861
Admissions	666,445⎫	
Births	113,548⎰	779,993

Viewed merely as cold and lifeless statistics these numbers would be meaningless. But beyond the realm of scientific analysis they interpret the story of one-hundred-thirty-one tabernacles from which Christ our Lord sends forth His benediction and consolation daily to some twenty thousand persons who are suffering in body or mind within these hospital walls. His guidance and blessing, too, accompany the approximately 7,100 students of paramedical groups and the 26,000 paid personnel whose responsibility lies in the care of these patients. Who can number the graces recorded in the Book of Life from the Sacraments alone administered over the days which weave a rounded century of years? The spirit of mercy has its source in God and converges in Him.

In passing, a tribute should be paid too to the visitation of the sick in the homes that the Sisters of Mercy outside the hospital sphere continue to make. In fact, in reading the Annals, chronicled as one of the first activities of almost every foundation was this work of mercy, even when later in some instances no hospitals were established. In the *Irish Catholic Directory* numerous Convents of Mercy mention it as a specific work; others record the story in their personal Annals. The Sisters of Mercy teaching in the elementary, secondary, and higher educational systems, wherever they may be, give an example to society of this Gospel precept of charity.

A list of hospitals conducted by the Sisters of Mercy throughout the world was compiled and may be found in Appendix C. In the Republic of Ireland alone the sisters operate eighty-four hospitals having a total capacity of 15,759 beds and located in 89 per cent of the counties. The four additional institutions in County Down of Northern Ireland in the United Kingdom bring the total beds to approximately 16,000. In other parts of the world may be found twenty-seven more institutions adding another 3,300 to the total beds and bassinets. The most southerly Mercy Hospital and perhaps the most southerly hospital in the world is that located in Dunedin, South Island, New Zealand. Certainly the dream of Mother McAuley for the sisters to have hospitals of their own within which to care for patients has had the hundredfold more than twice blessed.

b. Schools of Nursing

To Mercy Hospital, the first Catholic hospital in Chicago, goes also the honor of opening the first Catholic school of nursing in the state of Illinois in 1889.[18] But more important to Mercy history, it has the distinction likewise of being the first among many other schools of nursing conducted by the Sisters of Mercy throughout the world. This school has since given up its identity by name to become the Saint Xavier College School of Nursing, one of a number of schools within the College conducted by the Sisters of Mercy.

Mercy Hospital School of Nursing, Wilkes-Barre, Penn.
School opened in 1898; class of 1905

Mary's Hospital
ool of Nursing
an Francisco,
California
hool opened in
0; uniform 1905

St. Joseph's Infirmary School of Nursing, Atlanta, Georgia
School opened in 1900; uniform 1907 ff.

The Mater Hospital School of Nursing, Dublin; present uniform

St. Joseph Sanitarium, Dubuque, Iowa, 1887

Mercy Hospital, San Diego, California, 1890

St. Peter's Hospital, Albany, New York, 1869

Mercy Hospital, Baltimore, Maryland, 1874
New, modern institution in planning stage

St. Joseph Mercy Hospital, Clinton, Iowa, 1884

The Mater Hospital in Dublin was the second to open a school of nursing in 1891 entering upon its function of nursing education with a class of about twenty students.[19]

Within the twenty-five-year span from 1889 to 1914 the Sisters of Mercy in the United States opened 58 per cent of their diploma nursing programs which continue until the present. Others starting during that period have closed. In 1956 they conducted eight baccalaureate degree, one associate degree, two certificate, and forty-six diploma programs in nursing with an enrollment of 6,260 students. In addition, there were eight schools of practical or vocational nursing bringing the total number of students enrolled to approximately 6,500.

Ireland, England, Newfoundland, Australia, and New Zealand add another fifteen schools of nursing. In Ireland there are two programs of midwifery, two for infectious disease nursing, one for tuberculosis, and one for men nurses, as well as the eight regular programs in nursing recognized by the Board of Nursing. (A list of all these schools of nursing may be found in Appendix B.)

The variety of programs testify to an alertness for the needs of the sick and a willingness to keep abreast of sound educational trends in nursing. Here students may develop a consciousness that the destiny of an eternal society with God is at the root of man's social instinct and his individual dignity; they may see demonstrated that service to others may become a two-edged good when practiced in the spirit of One who washed the feet of a group of rather unresponsive followers; and they may increase their awareness of the concept that shared responsibility of many persons for the health of the patient implies recognition of the integrity of each one's contribution. When these lessons are learned and practiced the nurse takes her place in extending the spirit of mercy, God's mercy, to His suffering children.

PART VII

Epilogue

THE world continues to marvel at the success attending the work instituted by Catherine McAuley a century and a quarter ago. Begun as a tiny mustard seed in Ireland, the Congregation of Sisters had spread to England, Wales, and the Channel Islands within the first decade which coincided with the religious life span of the Foundress. After ten years the Community had extended to Newfoundland, the United States, Australia, Scotland, and New Zealand. The next half-century brought them to South America, Central America, South Africa, and the British West Indies. Within the last decade foundations have been made in Guam, India, East Africa, and the Philippine Islands.

Catherine McAuley believed that "she was but an instrument in the hands of God, and that if He called her away before [her Congregation] was nurtured into strength, He would Himself preside over its destiny."[1] Had she herself not said: "The Order is God's work, not mine. It will do just as well without me"?[2] That God accepted her trust is evident in the phenomenal growth of her community. Found in every English speaking country and on every continent, the Sisters of Mercy number more than 25,000. Half of their number labor in the United States. But wherever they are, the spiritual and corporal works of mercy are their apostolate, which they strive to perform in His Name and in imitation of Him.

In ministering to man's physical needs Mother McAuley aided him in regaining strength and courage toward achieving his final end. Because she recognized that man, struck down by illness, was entitled to the best in nursing care, she accepted the responsibility to prepare herself as well as possible for her work with the sick. With no formalized body of scientific and professional content at her disposal, the Foundress was willing to seek help from those more learned, concerned herself more with principles than with methods, and did patient-centered teaching in real-life situations. For this nursing pioneer the care of the sick was an art and good interpersonal relationships were but the expressions of supernatural charity. The very core of her nursing the whole person was that in him she "regarded the person of [her] Divine Master" expecting as she did "to meet [her] Divine Redeemer in every habitation."[3]

Just as the Foundress was an individual who followed in the path of the Divine Master in a way characteristic of herself alone, so each of her followers approaches her professional responsibilities with her own unique personality and within the frame of reference of the period in which she lives. It is a pattern fashioned on Christ and His Blessed Mother and modeled on the example of the saints.

Men pausing to consider the good going forward over the wide world that has its inspiration in Catherine McAuley may hear too the faint murmuring of her endless Magnificat re-echoing in the countless hearts that call her way a blessed one and join them in their song of praise to God.

APPENDIX A

McAULEYANA

GENERAL works telling the story of Mother Mary Catherine McAuley are not without number. The first brief sketch of her life was published within six years of her death and the last is yet to come off the press. But no one work was found which dealt solely or primarily with the Foundress' care of the sick.

The most essential sources for this study were the Constitutions of the Congregation and other publications which presented Mother McAuley's teaching in regard to the care of the sick. It was understandable that those writings which were more frequently accessible only to the members of the community should bear testimony to the unchanging spirit of the Congregation, and therefore be freely drawn upon for the study. Medical histories and journals supplied information concerning treatment of disease and the medical men with whom the Foundress labored. In addition to the above, other related works were chosen. From all of them were selected those passages which depicted the devotion of Mother McAuley to the sick poor, her interpretation of mercy, her motivating principle of serving Christ in the sick, and her skill in adapting to the ever-changing needs of society.

The first brief account of Mother McAuley's life appearing in 1847 has been attributed to the Very Reverend Myles Gaffney.[1] Early biographers quote from his account. Various

---

1. Mother Teresa Austin Carroll, *Life of Catherine McAuley* (St. Louis: The Vincentian Press, 1866), p. iii.

authors indicate that a portion of what Gaffney wrote appeared in the *Dublin Review* of 1847, some listing January and others March. A thorough search of both these issues failed to reveal to the writer the presence of this account. The March issue of the *Dublin Review* of the same year, however, carried her story as written by the Very Reverend Dominic Murphy. His name appears only in the separate index. It is said that he later incorporated the same story in a book published by him in 1865[2] but access to the book was not possible to the present writer. Biographer Murphy knew Mother McAuley well, witnessing her work and that of the sisters in the cholera epidemic which swept Dublin in 1832. This early sketch reads like a panegyric to the modern reader and must be placed in its historical setting to be appreciated.

Two other books, bearing the same title and year of publication, 1866, but having different publishers, are actually the same biography. The original edition lists the author as a member of the Order of Mercy;[3] the second names the author as Mother Austin Carroll.[4] In the latter book there is a final chapter which is new, and in the preface Mother Carroll acknowledges her indebtedness to a certain religious without naming her for the use of certain letters written by Mother McAuley. In the original text this religious had been identified as Mother Mary Francis Xavier Warde who brought the first Sisters of Mercy to the United States in 1843. This source for these letters is important, inasmuch as Mother Warde was associated with the Foundress in her work of mercy before it was established as a religious order, had been taught the fundamentals of the religious life by her, was in the first group professed at Baggot Street, and served as Mother McAuley's assistant from 1836 to 1837 at

---

2. Rev. **Dominic Murphy**, *Sketches of Irish Nunneries* (Dublin: James Duffy, 1865).

3. **Member of the Order of Mercy**, *Mother Mary Catherine McAuley* (New York: D. and J. Sadlier & Co., 1866).

4. Mother **Teresa Austin Carroll**, *Life of Catherine McAuley* (St. Louis: The Vincentian Press, 1866).

which time Mother Warde was commissioned to establish the first of her many foundations. The apparently earlier edition is important, too, because of the Introduction by the Reverend Richard Baptist O'Brien, Archdeacon of Limerick and formerly of All Hallows, Dublin. His message in the Introduction concentrated on the work done by the sisters in relation to the sick. In another work he stated:

"The author had the privilege of an early acquaintance with the foundress of the Sisters of Mercy, and has been all his life more or less intimate with the Institute. He has seen many brilliant specimens of sanctity and learning among the Sisterhood, and he has seen a devotion to the wants of ignorance and poverty which, to thinking people, is as much a miracle of Christian charity as the curing of the blind is a miracle of apostolic powers."[5]

Two years before Bishop O'Brien had written the Introduction for Mother Carroll's biography he had edited a biography of the Foundress written by Mother Mary Vincent Hartnett. In the preface of Mother Carroll's work, she said:

"About five years ago, Mother Mary V. Hartnett, of Roscommon, wrote a 'Memoir' of the Foundress from her own personal knowledge, and the narration of others. 'This was published, with a fine Introduction by the present Archbishop of Limerick. . . . This 'Memoir' contains two hundred pages, 12 mo. The preceding sketches are partially included in it."[6]

This biography by Mother Mary Vincent Hartnett was the first extensive life of Mother Mary Catherine McAuley. Few

---

5. Richard Baptist O'Brien, *Eight Days' Retreat for the Sisters of Mercy* (Dublin: John F. Fowler, 1868), in *Leaves from the Annals of the Sisters of Mercy*, I, 311.

6. Carroll, p. iv.

copies of this biography are extant and a later printing of it under another name is equally rare.

In 1887 the Sisters of Mercy in St. Louis edited what was titled a *Popular Life of Catherine McAuley* and in 1893 had the same book reissued by another publisher. The introduction stated that it was a "publication of the Dublin edition (1863)."[7] In another book, recording the work of the first fifty years of the Sisters of Mercy in St. Louis, reference was made to the publication of the *Popular Life* as a "reprint of the edition published in Ireland in 1863 by one of Mother McAuley's spiritual children."[8] The quotations which Mother Carroll credits to Mother M. Vincent Hartnett are present in this later edition. That these two printings are substantially the same was confirmed by those who possess the volume printed in Ireland.[9] Whenever reference was made to this biography in the study the author was listed as Mother Mary Vincent Hartnett.

This religious entered Baggot Street and went as a novice on the foundation to Limerick in 1838. Together with Mother McAuley the founding group reached their destination on the Feast of Our Lady of Mercy. Before leaving Limerick in December Mother McAuley wrote: "Sister M. Vincent Hartnett was professed yesterday."[10] In reference to her the *Annals of the Sisters of Mercy* state that she was:

"one of the most saintly women the foundress ever admitted. Her eminent religious spirit and highly cultured

---

7. Sisters of Mercy (eds.), *Popular Life of Catherine McAuley* (Baltimore: Baltimore Publishing Co., 1887 and New York: P. J. Kenedy, Excelsior Catholic Publishing House, 1893), p. 9.

8. Mary Constance Smith, *A Sheaf of Golden Years* 1856-1906 (New York: Benziger Brothers, 1906), p. 84.

9. Sister Mary Bertrand Degnan, R.S.M., Albany, New York, correspondence with the author, March 4, 1956.

10. Member of the Order of Mercy, *Leaves from the Annals of the Sisters of Mercy*, I, Ireland (New York: The Catholic Publication Society Co., 1881), p. 285.

mind qualified her for her new office [Superior of the new foundation in Roscommon in 1853]; indeed, much of the astonishing success of the Limerick house was due to the fine abilities and singular devotedness of this admirable woman. It would be quite impossible to imagine anything more perfect than Mother Mary Vincent's possession of Catherine McAuley's spirit."[11]

That the author of the *Memoirs* knew the Foundress personally is evident on every page. In this volume may be found many of the "sayings" of Mother McAuley that are used freely in more recent publications, but which in many instances are not documented except by tradition. Of the biographies quoted in the study this one was used most frequently.

In the intervening years other lives of Mother McAuley were published. These tell a story similar to that of Mother Austin Carroll. The biography by Barry published in Ireland in 1894[12] contains a few letters of the Foundress to Sister M. Aloysius not published until then; one contains the refreshing statement: "I think none so happy as I am."[13] Much later came the book by Simon who developed her theme from the viewpoint of confessor, apostle, virgin, and martyr.[14]

In 1949 Savage[15] presented a biography based primarily upon existing source materials, among which he listed a collection of more than two hundred letters written in Mother McAuley's own hand. While his work represents an authentic study of the Foundress of the Sisters of Mercy, he depicts but the character and life-story familiar to her followers. He

11. *Ibid.*, pp. 310-11.

12. K. M. Barry, *Catherine McAuley and the Sisters of Mercy*, (Dublin: Fallon and Son, 1894).

13. *Ibid.*, p. 101.

14. Sister Mary of the Angels Simon, R.S.M., *One Life in Christ* (New York: P. J. Kenedy & Sons, 1940).

15. Roland Burke Savage, S. J., *Catherine McAuley, the First Sister of Mercy* (Dublin: M. H. Gill and Son, Ltd., 1949).

is at variance with other biographers in establishing the year of her birth.

"Ireland's contribution to biographical works on Mother McAuley culminated in a thoroughly documented life entitled 'Catherine McAuley' written by Rev. R. Burke Savage, S.J. It is a work of the first importance, the fruit of years of patient research and may well be regarded as the Definitive Life."[16]

Soon to come off the press is another life under the title of *Mercy Unto Thousands*. For this biography the author, Sister Mary Bertrand Degnan,[17] also reviewed original source material. While this book was not ready for this study the author graciously made available to me letters of the Foundress and other primary source material. These plus her generous correspondence were of invaluable aid.

Other works exist which concentrate on the apostolate of Mother Mary Catherine McAuley. In 1931 Miley published a book the scope of which was indicated by the subtitle: foundress, educator, social welfare worker. The printed volume was the outgrowth of a thesis which had for its purpose:

"to portray respectfully and lovingly the Ideals of Mother McAuley as they lived in her and as they became incarnate in her Organization; to make known not what Mother McAuley had in common with other religious Foundresses, but what distinguished her from others. In short, to reveal her personality, her soul, her spirit."[18]

---

16. Sister of Mercy, "Mercy Girdles the Earth," *The Standard* (Dublin), January 6, 1956.

17. Sister Mary Bertrand Degnan, R.S.M., *Mercy Unto Thousands* (Westminster, Maryland: The Newman Press, 1957).

18. Sister Mary Hilda Miley, R.S.M., *The Ideals of Mother McAuley and Their Influence* (New York: P. J. Kenedy & Sons, 1931), p. 66.

In 1954 Lennon[19] made a compilation of the numerous
social works inspired and motivated by the Foundress and
now being performed by her spiritual children throughout
the world. This was no small task. It was helpful, particularly for the last portion of this work, in pointing to the
sources from which needed information could be obtained.
Lennon presented well what was described in the Foreword
by the Most Reverend Leo C. Byrne, Auxiliary Bishop of
St. Louis, in the following way:

"They would come, and they would come swiftly, armed
with the charity of Christ, and a great willingness to spend
themselves in the service of their fellowmen. The pattern,
too, was always the same—they were ready to teach the
little ones, to shepherd the orphans, to care for the aged, and
to minister to the sick."[20]

An interpretation of the spirit of Mother McAuley upon
which all these social works rest has been of interest to many
writers. O'Mahony[21] explained it in 1947 on the occasion of
the centenary of the Cork foundation of the Sisters of Mercy,
and Cooke[22] made it the subject of a dissertation in 1948.
The spirit, applied to nursing, was brought up for discussion
at an annual institute of the Sisters of Mercy in 1950,[23] and

---

19. Sister Mary Isidore Lennon, R.S.M., *Mother Catherine McAuley A Great Social Worker* (St. Louis: Sisters of Mercy of the Union, 1954).

20. *Ibid.*

21. J. E. O'Mahony (Father James, O.M.Cap.), "A Mission of Mercy," *Wherefore This Waste?* (London: Burns, Oates and Washbourne, Ltd., 1936), pp. 124-36.

22. Sister M. Lourdine Cooke, R.S.M., "The Contributions of Mother Mary Catherine McAuley to the Social Betterment of Society" (unpublished Master's dissertation, The Catholic University of America, Washington, D.C., 1948).

23. The Sisters of Mercy of the Union in the United States of America, "Proceedings of the Third Annual Institute in Hospital Administration and Nursing Education," (Cincinnati: The Sisters of Mercy, 1950).

was quoted by Wiley.[24] In 1921, McConomy[25] had accounted for the spirit of the Foundress by assembling her familiar sayings as ready references for the practice of virtue. Mullaly[26] in 1937 paid tribute to this spirit by epitomizing it in the word MERCY. Hence, it was necessary to review the essential meaning of Christian mercy. To interpret it as it was understood and practiced by the Foundress it was necessary to draw upon the wisdom of spiritual writers. Reference to these was made in the body of the thesis.

Schwitalla,[27] long associated with the Catholic Hospital Association of the United States and Canada, referred to the influence of Mother McAuley when writing of the century mark of the first Mercy Hospital in the United States. Flack,[28] tracing the nursing in Ireland from the pre-Christian period to the middle of the nineteenth century, recorded the work of the Sisters of Mercy. Walsh gave voice to the spirit of the Foundress by carrying her name into books of the history of nursing and magazine articles. His writing of her in *These Splendid Sisters* and his *History of Nursing* is very similar. Earlier he summarized his concept in these words:

"The spirit of Mother McAuley still prevails in the care of the poor, the education of the ignorant, and in the healing of the body in the hope of lifting up the mind, the heart and the soul."[29]

24. Sister Mary Louise Wiley, R.S.M., "A Survey in Religion and Religious Activities in Basic Schools of Nursing Conducted by the Religious Sisters of Mercy of the Union in the United States," (unpublished Master's dissertation, The Catholic University of America, Washington, D.C., 1951).

25. Sister Mary Louis McConomy, R.S.M., *The Spirit of Mary Catherine McAuley* (Oklahoma City: Mt. St. Mary's Academy, 1922).

26. Charles J. Mullaly, S.J., "The Spirit of Mother Mary Catherine McAuley," *Messenger of the Sacred Heart*, Vol. LXXII, No. 4, April, 1937.

27. Alphonse M. Schwitalla, S.J., "The Centenary of the Mercy Hospital, Pittsburgh," *Hospital Progress*, Vol. XXVIII, No. 4, April, 1947.

28. Hally Flack, "Nursing in Ireland from Pre-Christian Times to the Middle of the Nineteenth Century," *International Nursing Review*, Vol. VI, No. 5, September, 1931.

29. James J. Walsh, "Portraits from the Past: Catherine M'Auley," *Trained Nurse and Hospital Review*, LXX, No. 3 (March, 1923), p. 220.

Written since the thesis was published but available for its revision into book form was a short account by Sister M. Julian Baird[30] who presented for the modern reader in capsule form the measuring rod of mercy.

Data related to the medical men with whom Mother McAuley worked in caring for the sick was found in medical histories, primarily those of Walsh,[31] Garrison,[32] and Major,[33] and in the medical journals, the *Lancet* and *Medical Times and Gazette*. These journals also contained information regarding the cholera epidemic in which Mother Mc-Auley and her sisters cared for the sick. The Annals at the Mercy parent house in Dublin contained a section devoted to "Cholera 1832-1924." This was a compilation chiefly of newspaper Board of Health Reports of the 1832 epidemic and memoirs of the sisters concerning the care of the sick for the period. This section of the Annals was kindly made available to me for this study.

More liberally drawn upon, however, were those works in which Mother McAuley speaks for herself in her letters, instructions, conferences, and the Constitutions of her Congregation. This has been written to describe the letters of the Foundress:

"The prevailing characteristics of these letters are good sense, solid piety, intense love and compassion for the suffering and the ignorant, gratitude for the smallest acts of kindliness to her or hers, with holy and tender friendship for those united to her by spiritual kinship. Dashed off, as they were, in moments snatched from most absorbing occupations—some written in the stillness of night, some at the

---

30. Sister M. Julian Baird, R.S.M., "Servants of the Sick," *Messenger of the Sacred Heart*, Vol. XCII, No. 5 (May, 1957).

31. James J. Walsh, M.D., *Makers of Modern Medicine* (New York: Fordham University Press, 1907).

32. Fielding H. Garrison, *An Introduction to the History of Medicine* (Philadelphia: W. B. Saunders Company, 1917).

33. Ralph H. Major, M.D., *A History of Medicine* (Springfield, Illinois: Charles Thomas, Publisher, 1954).

couch of a dying Sister, some in the solitude of retreat, some
in the mirthful recreation hour—they may be regarded as a
compendium of her history and the history of her Institute
from 1836 to 1841, the more authentic because from her own
pen."[34]

Copies of her letters appear in the Annals of the Sisters
of Mercy, particularly the first two volumes which deal with
the foundations made in the lifetime of Mother McAuley
and continuing for the first half century.[35] The biographies
already listed which deal with primary source material carry
some of her letters. Still others appear either in the original
or microfilm form in the archives of various houses of the
Congregation. Unless otherwise indicated, quotations in this
study were taken from the collection made by Sister Mary
Bertrand Degnan of the Sisters of Mercy in Albany, New
York.

The instructions of Mother McAuley as used in the Congregation were made possible through their publication in
1888. The preface makes reference to their authenticity:

"These precepts have been used in manuscript form in
many of the convents in Ireland, but, in this country, a favored few only, had been in possession of the valued treas-
ure. Among these is the Community in Rochester, N.Y., from
whom a copy was obtained some years since, by the Sisters
of Mercy in St. Louis, Mo. Hence, before bringing out this
edition, the MS in hand was duly examined and declared
authentic, as Mother McAuley's spirit, that is the spirit of a
Religious Sister of Mercy, is breathed in every line. Moreover, one in the novitiate, Baggot Street Convent, Dublin,
and who is at present a member of a Community of Sisters
of Mercy in America, remembers having heard these same
instructions read from a manuscript for lecture in the noviti-

---

34. *Mercy Annals,* I, Ireland, 103.
35. *Ibid.,* Vol. 1, Ireland, 1881; Vol. II, England and the Colonies, 1883.

ate, Baggot Street Convent, before she came on the mission to the United States."[36]

These instructions are as familiar to the Sister of Mercy today as they were to the one who was privileged to hear them, undoubtedly, from the lips of the Foundress at Baggot Street.

Less known until recently were some instructions copied between 1832 and 1835 by the novices to whom Mother McAuley gave retreat conferences prior to the reception of the Holy Habit and later for the profession of vows. These notes were collected by Sister Mary Teresa Purcell who later, while still a novice, was sent to Tullamore, the second foundation and the first away from the Dublin vicinity. Mother McAuley remained with the beginning community for six weeks, and during this time provided the novice with personal direction in preparation for her profession which took place in May, 1836. Thus Sister M. Teresa had the opportunity to enlarge her earlier collection with her personal notes, and in later years when governing her community used them in her own instructions. She remained in Tullamore until her death in 1853 and there her private collection remained for almost a century. With the approval of her successors they were published in 1952. The editor made the following remark:

"These notes remain much as they appear in manuscript. In fact, with some modification, our plan follows Sister M. Teresa's policy as explained in her preface. The modification resulted largely from our use of a copy of her manuscript for annual retreat reading."[37]

---

36. Sister of Mercy (ed.), *Familiar Instructions of Rev. Mother McAuley* (St. Louis: Ev. E. Carreras, 1888), pp. v-vi.

37. Sister Mary Teresa Purcell, *Retreat Instructions of Mother Mary Catherine McAuley*, ed. Sisters of Mercy, Albany, New York (Westminster, Maryland: The Newman Press, 1952), p. 11.

In preparing her manuscript, Sister M. Teresa had said in her preface:

"The following instructions were given by our venerated foundress extempore at lectures and were written from memory afterwards by the sisters; hence they seem rather unconnected. As they contain an amount of solid, practical information useful to the sisters—above all, as we can find in almost every line of them the humble, simple spirit of our beloved Mother Foundress—we, her loving children, can make allowance, studying them in the spirit she gave them.

We set them all down as they were written by the different sisters. Fearing to rob them of the simplicity that is one of their best recommendations, we attempted no further arrangement and made no corrections."[38]

A number of Constitutions of the Sisters of Mercy were reviewed. These included a hand illuminated manuscript copied by the Kinsale community and sent to Mother Mary Baptist Russell when she brought the Sisters of Mercy from Ireland to San Francisco in 1854, and printed editions of 1872, 1926, and the present. The quotations used in the study were from the Dublin edition printed in 1872 and which carried the subheading: translated from the Italian.

A comparative study of the Mercy rule was made with those of the Presentation Sisters, the Ursuline Sisters, and the Rule of St. Augustine. The comparison of the four rules dealt primarily with the care of the sick as one of the works of the congregations or orders. In order to understand the effect of papal decrees upon religious orders, the work of Orth[39] was reviewed.

From this collection was selected the material which

---

38. *Ibid.*, pp. 16-17.
39. Clement Raymond Orth, O.M.C., *The Approbation of Religious Institutes* (Washington, D.C.: The Catholic University of America, 1931).

would assist best in writing the story of Mother Mary Catherine McAuley as it portrayed her devotion and care of the sick.

After this manuscript was ready for publication one more article appeared which began with the somewhat challenging statement that "the foundation of the Sisters of Mercy in 1831 . . . concerns the Catholic Church in the English-speaking world as few other events do."[40] The summary made of the work, and the spirit of the Foundress and the Congregation is an attempt to prove this statement. "Seen in the perspective of general Church history," the authors ends, "Catherine McAuley takes a high place with St. Macrina, the sister of St. Basil, St. Scholastica, the sister of St. Benedict, St. Clare, the friend of St. Francis Assisi, St. Louise de Marillac, the collaborator of St. Vincent de Paul, Blessed Julie Billiart, and St. Madeleine Sophie. St. Catherine of Siena has been called the 'great' Catherine. There are at least two. The rank of the Sisters of Mercy is also high. If the nineteenth century is the century of the religious women, the Sisters of Mercy are one of the most effective groups among them, perhaps unsurpassed in the English-speaking world. . . It is the glory of the Sisters of Mercy to be a very efficient unit in the forces of the militant Church."[41]

---

40. E. A. Ryan, S.J., "The Sisters of Mercy: An Important Chapter in Church History," *Theological Studies*, Vol. 18, No. 2 (June, 1957), 254.

41. *Ibid.*, pp. 269-70.

APPENDIX B

PROGRAMS IN NURSING CONDUCTED BY THE SISTERS OF MERCY LISTED BY COUNTRY

TABLE I
PROGRAMS IN NURSING IN THE UNITED STATES IN CHRONOLOGICAL ORDER OF FOUNDATION
(Footnotes appear at end of Table. See also Notes, pp. 154-69.)

	Year	Name of Program	Di	Ce	AS	BS	PV	City	State	No.1
	1889	Mercy2						Chicago	Ill.	
1	1893	Mercy3	x					Pittsburgh	Penna.	333
2	1893	Sacred Heart	x					Manchester	N. H.	40
3	1896	Mercy	x					Council Bluffs	Ia.	52
4	1898	Mercy	x					Wilkes-Barre	Penna.	150
5	1899	Mercy	x					Baltimore	Md.	142
6	1899	Mercy	x					Des Moines	Ia.	109
7	1900	St. Mary's4	x					San Francisco	Calif.	223
8	1900	St. Peter's	x					Albany	N. Y.	148
9	1900	St. Joseph Mercy	x					Dubuque	Ia.	131
10	1900	St. Joseph's	x					Atlanta	Ga.	98
11	1902	St. Joseph Mercy	x					Sioux City	Ia.	265
12	1902	Mercy	x					Denver	Colo.	104
13	1902	St. Joseph's	x					Savannah	Ga.	69
14	1903	Mercy	x					San Diego	Calif.	151
15	1903	St. John's	x					Joplin	Mo.	59
16	1905	St. John's	x					St. Louis	Mo.	224
17	1905	St. Joseph's	x					Hot Springs	Ark.	70
18	1906	Mercy	x					Charlotte	N. C.	130
19	1906	Mercy	x					Hamilton	Ohio	87
20	1906	Mercy	x					Watertown	N. Y.	74
21	1906	St. Edward	x					Fort Smith	Ark.	58
22	1910	St. Joseph's	x					Phoenix	Ariz.	163
23	1910	St. Catherine's	x					Omaha	Neb.	141
24	1911	Mercy	x					Johnstown	Penna.	122

25	1911	St. John's	x		Springfield	Mo.	95
26	1911	Mercy	x		Janesville	Wis.	50
27	1914	Mercy	x		Iowa City	Ia.	93
28	1917	Mercy	x		Scranton	Penna.	83
29	1918	Misericordia	x		Philadelphia	Penna.	198
30	1918	Mercy	x		Toledo	Ohio	188
31	1919	St. Rita's	x		Lima	Ohio	114
32	1919	St. Anthony Mercy	x		Pocatello	Idaho	25
33	1920	Mercy	x		Portland	Me.	135
34	1921	Warner Brown	x		El Dorado	Ark.	54
35	1922	St. Joseph Mercy	x		Aurora	Ill.	55
36	1924	Mercy	x		Oklahoma City	Okla.	69
37	1925	Mercy	x		New Orleans	La.	94
38	1928	Mercy	x		Buffalo	N. Y.	185
39	1930	St. Mary's Memorial	x		Knoxville	Tenn.	111
40	1934	Mercy	x		Detroit	Mich.	671
41	1934	St. Xavier College		x			50
		School of Nursing		x	Chicago	Ill.	71
42	1935	Mercy Central	x		Grand Rapids	Mich.	254
43	1939	St. James Mercy	x		Hornell	N. Y.	50
44	1941	Mercy College Division of Nursing		x	Detroit	Mich.	142
45	1942	Fitzgerald Mercy	x		Darby	Penna.	187
46	1943	Mercy-Street Memorial	x		Vicksburg	Miss.	58
47	1947	Mercy	x		Valley City	N. D.	57
48	1948	Mt. St. Agnes College Division of Nursing		x	Mt. Wash.	Md.	43
49	1948	Salve Regina College Division of Nursing		x	Newport	R. I.	41
50	1948	Mount Mercy College Department of Nursing		x	Pittsburgh	Penna.	85
51	1948	Mercedarian School for Practical Nurses		x	Marshalltown	Ia.	31
52	1949	Mercy	x		Fort Scott	Kan.	71
53	1949	Brial Cliff College[5] Department of Nursing[6]		x	Sioux City	Ia.	27
54	1950	Mercy Central School for Practical Nurses		x	Springfield	Ohio	44
55	1951	St. Ambrose College[5] Division of Nursing		x	Davenport	Ia.	127
56	1951	Mount Mercy College Department of Nursing		x	Cedar Rapids	Ia.	102
57	1952	Mercedarian School of Practical Nursing		x	Scranton	Penna.	26
58	1952	Mercy School of Vocational Nursing		x	Laredo	Tex.	15
59	1953	McAuley School of Practical Nursing		x	Pontiac	Mich.	52

60	1953	Villanova University[5] School of Nursing	x		Villanova	Penna.	67
61	1954	Univ. of San Francisco[5] School of Nursing	x		San Francisco	Calif.	100
62	1955	Mercy School of Practical Nursing		x	Nampa	Idaho	14
63	1955	Mercy School of Vocational Nursing		x	Brownsville	Tex.	20
64	1956	Mercy School of Practical Nursing		x	Springfield	Mo.	25

---

1. Di—Diploma three year program.

   CE—Certificate or diploma from a college granted at the end of three years.

   AS—Associate Degree from a college at the end of two years.

   BS—Baccalaureate Degree at the end of four years.

   PV—Practical or vocational nurse, twelve-month program.

   No.—Number of students enrolled.

2. This school is mentioned by name in order to give priority to the year it was founded as a diploma program, but it is not included in the total count. Since it exists now under another name, the data may be found under 41—Ce in this Table.

3. The name "School of Nursing" completes the title of each school listed unless otherwise indicated.

4. With the students graduating in 1959 this school of nursing will relinquish its identity as a diploma program. Students will be enrolled only in the baccalaureate degree program of the University of San Francisco School of Nursing. See 61—BS in this Table.

5. The academic institution does not belong to the Sisters of Mercy but the Sisters chair the school of nursing and cooperate by supplying faculty and clinical facilities.

6. The Department of Nursing is to be discontinued with graduation of the last class admitted to the Department in September, 1955.

TABLE II
PROGRAMS IN NURSING IN COUNTRIES OTHER THAN THE UNITED STATES

	Name of Institution Conducting School	City	County or State	Country
1	Mater Misericordiae Hospital	Dublin	Dublin	Ireland
2	Jervis Street Hospital	Dublin	Dublin	Ireland
3	St. Michael's Hospital	Dun Laoghaire	Dublin	Ireland
4	Mercy Hospital	Cork	Cork	Ireland
5	South Charitable Infirmary[1]	Cork	Cork	Ireland
6	St. Finbarr's Hospital[1 2 3]	Cork	Cork	Ireland
7	Regional Hospital[1 2]	Galway	Galway	Ireland
8	Regional Hospital	Doora-doyle	Limerick	Ireland
9	Mater Infirmoorum Hospital	Belfast	Down	Ireland
10	Hospital of St. John and St. Elizabeth	London	London	England
11	St. Clare's Mercy Hospital	St. John's		Newfoundland
12	Mater Misericordiae Hospital	Auckland	N. Island	New Zealand
13	Mater Misericordiae Hospital	Brisbane	Queensland	Australia
14	Mater Misericordiae Hospital	Mackay	Queensland	Australia
15	Mater Misericordiae Hospital	Sydney	N. S. Wales	Australia

---

1. Also conducts a course in midwifery.
2. Also conducts a course in infectious disease nursing.
3. Also offers a program for men nurses.

APPENDIX C

HOSPITALS CONDUCTED BY THE SISTERS OF MERCY LISTED BY COUNTRY

TABLE III
HOSPITALS OF SISTERS OF MERCY IN THE UNITED STATES

State and City	Name of Institution	Year	Beds	Bass.
ALABAMA				
Daphne	Villa Mercy-chronic & convalescent	1949	29	—
Mobile	Blessed Martin de Porres Hospital	1950	35	10
ARIZONA				
Phoenix	St. Joseph's Hospital	1894	325	80
ARKANSAS				
Brinkley	Mercy Hospital	1953	46	12
El Dorado	Warner Brown Hospital	1920	130	29
Fort Smith	St. Edward's Mercy Hospital	1905	153	40
Fort Smith	Mercy Villa-convalescent & chronic	——	25	—
Hot Springs	St. Joseph's Hospital	1888	220	30
CALIFORNIA				
Bakersfield	Mercy Hospital	1910	178	30
Oxnard	St. John's Hospital	1912	75	22
Red Bluff	St. Elizabeth's Hospital	1908	40	8
Redding	Mercy Hospital	1944	72	20
Sacramento	Mercy Hospital	1895	325	60
San Diego	Mercy Hospital	1890	335	94
San Francisco	St. Mary's Hospital	1855	327	55
San Francisco	Notre Dame Hospital	1946	150	—
COLORADO				
Denver	Mercy Hospital	1901	250	40
Durango	Mercy Hospital	1882	100	20
CONNECTICUT				
West Hartford	St. Agnes Maternity Home	1914	8	8
GEORGIA				
Atlanta	St. Joseph's Infirmary	1881	300	40

143

Savannah	St. Joseph's Hospital	1875	116	26
IDAHO				
Nampa	Mercy Hospital	1919	85	20
Pocatello	St. Anthony's Mercy Hospital	1918	100	24
ILLINOIS				
Aurora	Mercyville Sanitarium	1915	172	–
Aurora	St. Joseph Mercy Hospital	1911	104	28
Chicago	Mercy Hospital	1852	356	40
Chicago	Misericordia Home—Maternity & Ped.	1921	80	—
De Kalb	St. Mary's Hospital	1922	54	13
INDIANA				
Dyer	Our Lady of Mercy Hospital	1942	200	—
Hammond	St. Ann's Home—Convalescent & Chronic	1936	120	—
IOWA				
Algona	St. Ann Hospital	1949	40	12
Anamosa	Mercy Hospital	1893	34	8
Cedar Rapids	Mercy Hospital	1900	222	30
Centerville	St. Joseph's Mercy Hospital	1903	50	12
Clinton	St. Joseph's Mercy Hospital	1884	100	25
Council Bluffs	Mercy Hospital	1903	188	30
Council Bluffs	St. Bernard's Hospital	1887	208	—
Cresco	St. Joseph's Mercy Hospital	1911	35	8
Davenport	Mercy Hospital	1869	330	45
Des Moines	Mercy Hospital	1894	200	30
Des Moines	Bishop Drumm Home for Aged—Chronic	1939	90	—
Dubuque	St. Joseph Mercy Hospital	1879	348	35
Dubuque	St. Joseph Sanitarium	1887	155	—
Fort Dodge	St. Joseph Mercy Hospital	1908	175	25
Iowa City	Mercy Hospital	1878	190	33
Marshalltown	Mercy Hospital	1902	84	20
Mason City	St. Joseph's Mercy Hospital	1916	218	35
Olewein	Mercy Hospital	1926	58	15
Sioux City	St. Joseph's Mercy Hospital	1890	425	40
Waverly	St. Joseph Mercy Hospital	1904	46	10
KANSAS				
Fort Scott	Mercy Hospital	1887	173	20
Fredonia	St. Margaret's Mercy Hospital	1950	42	10
Hutchinson	St. Elizabeth's Mercy Hospital	1920	107	27
Independence	Mercy Hospital	1927	56	14
KENTUCKY				
Morganfield	Our Lady of Mercy Hospital	1945	25	7
Owensboro	Our Lady of Mercy Hospital	1948	50	15
LOUISIANA				
New Orleans	Mercy Hospital	1924	191	44
MAINE				
Houlton	Madigan Memorial Hospital	1915	54	13
Portland	Mercy Hospital	1918	217	40
MARYLAND				
Baltimore	Mercy Hospital	1874	300	55

Govans	Mercy Villa—Chronic & Convalescent	1920	22	—
MICHIGAN				
Ann Arbor	Mercywood Sanitarium	1925	125	—
Ann Arbor	St. Joseph's Mercy Hospital	1911	297	54
Battle Creek	Leila Y. Post Montgomery Hospital	1927	175	25
Bay City	Mercy Hospital	1899	303	50
Cadillac	Mercy Hospital	1908	125	12
Detroit	Mt. Carmel Mercy Hospital	1939	538	125
Detroit	St. Joseph Mercy Hospital	1923	225	30
Grayling	St. Mary's Hospital	1893	346	55
Grand Rapids	Mercy Hospital	1911	45	8
Jackson	Mercy Hospital	1915	125	30
Lansing	St. Lawrence Hospital	1920	275	60
Manistee	Mercy Hospital	1889	100	12
Muskegon	Mercy Hospital	1903	160	30
Pontiac	St. Joseph Mercy Hospital	1927	310	77
Port Huron	Mercy Hospital	1954	100	12
MISSISSIPPI				
Vicksburg	Mercy-Street Memorial Hospital	1943	140	17
MISSOURI				
Joplin	St. John's Hospital	1899	150	26
St. Louis	St. John's Hospital	1871	362	74
Springfield	St. John's Hospital	1891	232	50
Springfield	Mercy Infirmary—Convalescent	1952	175	—
MONTANA				
Kalispell	Kalispell General Hospital	1910	66	12
NEBRASKA				
Omaha	St. Catherine's Hospital	1910	200	40
Omaha	St. Vincent's Home for Aged Chronic	1953	200	—
NEW HAMPSHIRE				
Manchester	Sacred Heart Hospital	1892	146	24
Manchester	Our Lady of Grace Convalescent Home	1946	20	—
NEW JERSEY				
Sea Isle City	Mercy Hospital	1953	25	7
NEW YORK				
Albany	St. Peter's Hospital	1869	294	—
Batavia	St. Jerome Hospital	1917	135	18
Buffalo	Mercy Hospital	1904	360	75
Gabriels	Sanitorium Gabriels—Tuberculosis	1895	75	—
Gabriels	St. Margaret's Home—Convalescent & Chronic	—	56	—
Hornell	St. James Mercy Hospital	1890	130	18
Kenmore	Kenmore Mercy Hospital	1949	112	30
Port Jervis	St. Francis Hospital	1915	57	8
Spring Valley	St. Vincent de Paul Convalescent Home	1902	30	—
Tupper Lake	Mercy General Hospital	1918	35	10
Watertown	Mercy Hospital	1894	137	23

NO. CAROLINA

Asheville	St. Joseph's Hospital	1900	137	38
Charlotte	Mercy Hospital	1906	280	50

NO. DAKOTA

Devils Lake	Mercy Hospital	1902	75	15
Valley City	Mercy Hospital	1928	108	18
Williston	Mercy Hospital	1920	100	25

OHIO

Cincinnati	Our Lady of Mercy Hospital	1942	54	20
Coldwater	Our Lady of Mercy Hospital	1950	40	20
Hamilton	Mercy Hospital	1892	300	45
Lima	St. Rita's Hospital	1918	293	50
Springfield	Mercy Hospital	1950	300	60
Tiffin	Mercy Hospital	1913	90	20
Toledo	Mercy Hospital	1918	289	60
Toledo	St. Charles Hospital	1953	201	30
Urbana	Mercy Memorial Hospital	1951	50	20

OKLAHOMA

Oklahoma City	Mercy Hospital Oklahoma City General	1916	150	25

OREGON

Coos Bay	McAuley Hospital	1939	74	12
North Bend	Mercy Home for Aged & Convalescent	1906	40	—
Portland	Mt. St. Joseph Home for Aged & Chronic	1901	165	—
Roseburg	Mercy Hospital	1909	50	15

PENNSYLVANIA

Darby	Thomas M. Fitzgerald-Mercy Hospital	1933	370	100
Downington	Villa St. John Vianney	1946	16	—
Du Bois	Du Bois Hospital	1898	95	18
Johnstown	The Mercy Hospital	1910	220	50
Philadelphia	Misericordia Hospital	1918	280	50
Pittsburgh	Mercy Hospital	1847	683	65
Scranton	Mercy Hospital	1917	100	25
Scranton	St. Mary's Hospital	1916	70	15
Wilkes-Barre	Mercy Hospital	1898	200	30

TENNESSEE

Knoxville	St. Mary's Memorial Hospital	1930	270	30

TEXAS

Brownsville	Mercy Hospital	1917	90	24
Laredo	Mercy Hospital	1894	76	28
Slaton	Mercy Hospital	1929	31	10

WISCONSIN

Janesville	Mercy Hospital	1907	200	35

Mercy Hospital, Manistee, Michigan, 1889

St. John's Hospital, St. Louis, Missouri, 1871

St. Joseph's Convalescent Home, Bournemouth, England

Mercy Hospital, E. Melbourne, Australia

Mercy Hospital, Cork, Ireland

Mater Infirmorum Hospital, Belfast, North Ireland

St. Clare's Mercy Hospital, St. John's, Newfoundland

Mater Misericordiae Hospital, Auckland, New Zealand

TABLE IV
HOSPITALS OF THE SISTERS OF MERCY
IN IRELAND[1]

County and City	Name or Type of Hospital[2]	Year	Beds	Ow.[3]
CARLOW				
Carlow	Carlow District Hospital*		19	
Carlow	Sacred Heart County Home**		220	
CAVAN				
Cavan	St. Felim's County Medical		191	
	Hospital and County Home		146	
Cavan	County Surgical Hospital		70	
CLARE				
Ennis	County Home		338	
Ennis	Ennis Fever Hospital		38	
Kilrush	Kilrush District Hospital		38	
CORK				
Bantry	Bantry District Hospital—St. Joseph's*		51	
Castletownbere	Castletownbere District Hospital		28	
Clonakilty	Clonakilty District Hospital*		40	
Clonakilty	County Home		280	
Cork	Mercy Hospital	1857	147	x
Cork	St. Finbarr's Hospital (Teaching)		1363	
Cork	St. Raphael's Preventorium (Tuberculosis)		50	xxx
Cork	South Charitable Infirmary and Co.			
	Hospital (Teaching)		134	a
Kinsale	Kinsale District Hospital		24	
Midleton	Midleton District Home and Hospital		260	
Skibbereen	Skibbereen District Hospital*		45	
Youghal	Youghal District Hospital*		45	
DONEGAL				
Ballyshannon	St. Brigid's District Hospital		33	
Ballyshannon	Sheil Hospital		40	a
Donegal	District Hospital		46	
Donegal	Fever Hospital		17	
Glenties	Glenties District Hospital*		38	
Stranorlar	County Home**		296	
DOWN				
Beechmount	Our Lady's Hospice Hospital	1932	100	x
Belfast	Mater Infirmorum Hospital	1883-1900	190	x
Belfast	Mater Maternity Unit	1939	24	x
Belfast	St. John's Private Nursing Home	1912	30	x
DUBLIN				
Dublin	Beaumont Convalescent Home	1900	129	x
Dublin	Jervis Street Hospital (Teaching Charitable Infirmary)	1854	242	a
Dublin	The Mater Misericordiae Hospital	1852	500	x

Dublin	St. Kevin's Hospital		1900 xx
Dun Laoghaire	Our Lady of Lourdes Hospital (Tuberculosis)	1918	139 x
Dun Laoghaire	St. Michael's Hospital		136 x
Rathfarnham	St. Mary's Preventorium (Tuberculosis)	1943	75 x
GALWAY			
Clifden	District Hospital*		40
Galway	Galway Regional Hospital (Teaching)		525
Loughrea	St. Brendan's County Home		455
KERRY			
Dingle	St. Elizabeth's District Hospital*	1889	49
Killarney	County Home		537
Killarney	District Hospital		48
Killarney	St. Anne's Isolation Hospital		44
Listowel	St. Brigid's District Hospital*	1883	33
Tralee	St. Catherine's County Hospital	1874	173
KILDARE			
Athy	St. Vincent's Hospital**		285
KILKENNY			
Kilkenny	County Hospital		150
LEITRIM			
Manorhamilton	Our Lady's County Hospital		61
LIMERICK			
Croom	St. Nessan's Hospital		200
Dooradoyle	Limerick Regional Hospital	1952	286
Limerick	City Home and Hospital		493 xx
Newcastle West	County Home		369
LONGFORD			
Edgeworthstown	Our Lady's Nursing Home		25 x
Longford	County Home and County Medical Hospital		230
Longford	Mount Carmel Hospital (Tuberculosis)		39
LOUTH			
Ardee	District Hospital*		61
Drogheda	District Hospital*		240
Dundalk	Blessed Oliver Plunkett Hospital		228
Dundalk	Louth County Hospital		38
MAYO			
Ballina	District Hospital		84
Castlebar	Mayo County Home***		308
Swinford	District Hospital*		20
Swinford	Mayo County Fever Hospital		30
MEATH			
Navan	Meath County Hospital		192
Trim	County Home and Maternity Hospital**		300
Trim	Lourdes Orthopaedic Hospital		12
MONAGHAN			
Castleblaney	County Home**		240
Monaghan	County Hospital		150

OFFALY

Tullamore	Offaly County Home and Fever Hospital**	27
		285
Tullamore	Offaly County Hospital	107
Tullamore	St. Vincent's Hospital (Tuberculosis)	22

SLIGO

Ballytivinan	The County Home***	295

TIPPERARY

Cashel	Our Lady's County Hospital	90
Cashel	St. Patrick's County Home	364
Clogheen	Clogheen District Hospital	24
Clonmel	County Medical and Maternity Hospital	103
Nenagh	St. Joseph's General Hospital	83
Thurles	Hospital of the Assumption County Home	347
Tipperary	St. Vincent's Tipperary District Hospital	58

WATERFORD

Dungarven	County Home**	266
Dungarven	District Hospital*	38
Waterford	St. Patrick's County Hospital	229
Waterford	County Waterford Fever Hospital	62

WESTMEATH

Athlone	St. Vincent's District Hospital	66
Mullingar	County Home**	220
Mullingar	Westmeath County Hospital	93

WICKLOW

Rathdrum	St. Kevin's Sanatorium (Tuberculosis)	38
Rathdrum	St. Colman's Hospital	279

---

1. Compiled from Irish Catholic Directory and data supplied by the Hospitals Commission of Dublin.
2. Type of Hospital:
   District Hospital—medical, surgical, obstetrical unless starred.
   *—ordinarily implies a greater number of services; in some instances, general.
   County Home—chronic sick unless starred.
   *—chronic sick plus obstetrics.
   ***—varies from either of the above.
3. Ownership:
   The ownership unless otherwise designated is the county.
   Symbols for other ownership:
   x—Sisters of Mercy.
   xx—Municipal.
   xxx—Red Cross.
   a—Public (voluntary) or (semi-voluntary).

TABLE V
HOSPITALS OF THE SISTERS OF MERCY OTHER THAN IN THE UNITED STATES AND IRELAND

COUNTRY COUNTY OR STATE City	Name of Institution	Year	Beds	Bass.
NEWFOUNDLAND				
St. John's	St. Clare's Mercy Hospital	1922	140	22
ENGLAND				
DERBYSHIRE				
Ednaston, Brailsford	St. Mary's Nursing Home	1948	20	—
ESSEX				
Clacton-on-Sea	St. Michael's Convalescent Home	1946	48	—
LONDON				
London	Hospital of St. John & St. Elizabeth	1856	175	—
SOUTHAMPTON				
Bournemouth	St. Joseph's Convalescent Home	1888	76	—
YORKSHIRE				
Whitley, Chubb Hill	Mercy Nursing Home	1910	16	—
SCOTLAND				
GLASGOW				
Baillieston	St. Catherine's Home	1953	24	—
NEW ZEALAND				
NORTH ISLAND				
Auckland	Mater Misericordiae Hospital	1900	148	12
Palmerston	Mater Misericordiae Hospital	1950	45	—
SOUTH ISLAND				
Dunedin	Mater Misericordiae Hospital	1936	23	—
AUSTRALIA				
NEW SOUTH WALES				
Albury	Mercy Hospital	1944	21	10
Cootamundra	Sacred Heart & St. Catherine's Hospital	1925	68	—
Forbes	Mater Misericordiae Hospital	1951	11	6
Sydney	Mater Misericordiae Hospital	1906	353	80
Waratah	Mater Misericordiae Hospital	1922	247	50
Young	Sacred Heart Hospital	1923	72	—
Young	St. Joseph's Hospice	1920	15	—
QUEENSLAND				
Brisbane	Mater Misericordiae Hospital	1906	405	—
Bundaberg	Mater Misericordiae Hospital	1946	43	—
Mackay	Mater Misericordiae Hospital	1925	76	21

Rockhampton	Mater Misericordiae Hospital	1934	123	12
Townsville	Mater Misericordiae Hospital	1945	29	—
VICTORIA				
Melbourne	Mercy Hospital	1935	173	45
WESTERN AUSTRALIA				
Perth	St. Anne's Hospital	1937	141	75
SOUTH AMERICA				
BRITISH GUIANA[1]				
Mahaica	Leprosarium	1935	360	2
Georgetown	St. Joseph's Mercy Hospital	1945	124	12
INDIA				
Jameshedpur[2][3]	Dalal Memorial Hospital	1952	80	—

---

1. Mission of the Sisters of Mercy of the Union of the U.S.A., Scranton Province.

2. Mission of the Sisters of Mercy—Merion, Pennsylvania Generalate.

3. Mission clinics have been opened in 1956 and 1957 in Africa and the Philippine Islands by other Mercy groups.

APPENDIX D

Tilbury Dock

The people of London gathered to cheer
The heroes of Sevastópol
As the Grenadier Guards came home from war
In ships from Constantinople.
The Grenadier Guards stepped on Tilbury Dock,
Ready to march to the Tower,
When an order ran through their thinned, red lines
To set back their marching hour.

"We wait for the Sisters," the colonel said;
"They tended our sick, and they buried our dead.
They stood with us, fearless and unafraid,
Behind the charge of the Light Brigade.
Today, in England's triumphal hour,
They march before us to London Tower."

The Grenadier Guards gave the Mercy nuns,
Who nursed them at Sevastópol,
A cheer beyond any they ever heard
In streets in Constantinople;
But the London crowd at Tilbury Dock
Murmured in horrid groaning,
And from the streets picked the paving blocks
To hold in their hands for stoning.
"We march with the Sisters," the colonel said;

"The Sisters of Mercy will march at our head,
Or the Grenadier Guards will not march at all
To Tower, or Palace, or even Whitehall.
Until the last of the Guards is dead,
We shall honor the Sisters," the colonel said.

The band struck up with mighty roar
As the thinned, red lines stood ready,
And twelve black-robed Sisters passed through the ranks
That held for them, valiant and steady.
Then, falling in step to *Brittania Rules,*
And moving in courage solemn,
The Grenadier Guards marched to London Tower,
And the Sisters headed the column.

Long years have gone since those Grenadier Guards
Came home from far Sevastópol;
In other wars other Guardsmen marched
Through the streets of Constantinople;
But still in barracks, the story is told,
With every Guardsman lifting his head
To say, "We shall honor these Sisters twelve
Until the last of the Guards is dead."

MARY SYNON[1]

---

1. Sister M. Thomas Aquinas, O.P., M.A. and Mary Synon, LL.D., *This is Our Heritage* (Boston: Ginn and Company, 1943), pp. 359-60. Reproduced by permission of the author, Mary Synon, and Ginn and Company, publishers.

NOTES

PART I. HISTORY TELESCOPED

1. James J. Walsh, *World's Debt to the Irish*, p. 120. *cf.* Catholic Encyclopedia, Vol. VIII, 614.
2. J. Minor Gwynn, *Curriculum Principles and Social Trends*, p. 1.
3. J. L. Hammond and Barbara Hammond, *The Town Labourer*, p. 180.
4. Roland Burke Savage, S.J., *A Valiant Dublin Woman*, p. 20.
5. *Times*, July 12, 1847, quoted in J. L. Hammond and Barbara Hammond, *The Age of the Chartists: 1832-1854*, p. 23.
6. Carlton J. H. Hayes, *A Political and Social History of Modern Europe*, I, 281-82.
7. John Morley (ed.), *Burke: English Men of Letters*, p. 101.
8. *The Works of the Right Honorable Burke*, IV, 221.
9. Charles William Fitzwilliam and Richard Bourke (eds.), *Correspondence of the Right Honourable Edmund Burke*, IV, 274.
10. Hammond and Hammond, *The Town Labourer*, pp. 151-52.
11. Savage, *A Valiant Dublin Woman*, p. 199.
12. Andrew Bell, *Historical Sketches of Feudalism*, p. 259.
13. Savage, *A Valiant Dublin Woman*, pp. 49-140.

PART II. A DESTINY FASHIONED

1. Roland Burke Savage, S.J., *Catherine McAuley, the First Sister of Mercy,* p. 420.
2. Sister M. Bertrand Degnan, R.S.M., Albany, New York, Correspondence with the author, March 7, 1956.
3. Sister Rosanna Barker, S.C., "Mother Margaret Cecilia George, First Superior of the Sisters of Charity of Cincinnati, O.," p. 113. Quoting letter from the Rt. Rev. Edward Doorly, Bishop of Elphin, dated November 16, 1942.
4. Savage, *Catherine McAuley,* p. 21.
5. Mother M. Vincent Hartnett, *Memoirs,* pp. 19-20.
6. Savage, *Catherine McAuley,* p. 22.
7. Hartnett, pp. 25-26.
8. Documented copy of William Callaghan's will, Archives of the Sisters of Mercy, Albany, New York.
9. "Nuns' Home Coming," *The Standard* (Dublin), October 7, 1955, XXVII:195.
10. "Catherine McAuley—the Heiress from Coolock," *Irish Independent,* December 12, 1955.
11. Mother Teresa Austin Carroll, *Life of Catherine McAuley,* p. 75.
12. Savage, *Catherine McAuley,* p. 45.
13. Annals of the Sisters of Mercy, Kinsale, Ireland, photostatic copy Burlingame archives.
14. Letter to the Rev. F. L'Estrange, O.D.C., September 10, 1828.
15. Rev. Dominic Murphy, "The Order of Mercy and Its Foundress," *Dublin Review* XXII:13 (March, 1847), p. 11.
16. Hartnett, p. 57.
17. Bessie R. Belloc, "Catherine McAuley," *Historic Nuns,* p. 86.
18. Hartnett, p. 43.
19. *Ibid.,* p. 71.

20. Reverend Dr. Michael Blake quoted in Savage, *Catherine McAuley*, p. 103.
21. *Retreat Instructions of Mother Mary Catherine McAuley*, comp. Sister Mary Teresa Purcell. Edited by Sisters of Mercy, Albany, New York, p. 24.
22. Savage, *Catherine McAuley*, p. 2.
23. Letter to Miss Gibson, March 28, 1841.
24. Letter to Rev. Gerald Doyle, P.P. Naas, September 8, 1836 (P.P. was an abbreviation for parish priest).
25. James J. Walsh, *These Splendid Sisters*, p. 116.
26. From Steele's "Spectator": ". . . Sir Roger de Coverly. His great-grandfather was inventor of that famous country dance which is called after him."
27. *Annals of the Sisters of Mercy*, ed. Member of the Order of Mercy [Mother Teresa Austin Carroll], in four volumes, II, 63.
28. Letter to Sister M. Francis with envelope dated April 21, 1841.
29. Letter to Sister M. Francis, July 19, 1841.
30. Letter to S.M.A. [Sister Mary Anne Doyle], September 24, 1841.
31. *Morning Register* (Dublin), November 15, 1841. Albany archives.
32. H. A. McHugh, D.C.L., "The Making of a Mother's Heart," *The Redemptorist Record*, XIX, No. 6 (November-December, 1955), p. 177.
33. Letter to Sister M. Aloysius quoted in K. M. Barry, *Catherine McAuley and the Sisters of Mercy*, p. 101.

PART III. A WAY OF MERCY

1. Tertiary of the Order, *Our Lady's Order of Ransom Called Mercy*, pp. 9-10.
2. Katherine Burton, *So Surely Anchored*, p. 25.
3. Carroll, p. 225.
4. Peter of St. Cecelio, Rev. O.D.M., *Annales Del Orden*

De Descalcos De N. S. De La Merced, p. 140. Translated from the Spanish.

William Thomas Walsh in *Isabella of Spain* in a note on p. 501 covering Ch. XXVI, 3, indicates that Marius Andre mentions friars accompanying Columbus without documenting his source "for this unusual opinion."

Marius Andre, in his life of Columbus, (Cf. p. 102) says there were a total crew of ninety men plus another group of about thirty persons some of whom he mentions by name. In this listing he has "several friars from Palos."

5. Samuel Eliot Morison, *Admiral of the Ocean Sea,* p. 404.
6. Rev. Sante Gattuso, O.D.M., LeRoy, New York, St. Raymond Nonnatus Seminary, correspondence with the author, 1956 and 1957.
7. Peter of St. Cecelio, p. 140.
8. William H. Prescott, *History of the Conquest of Mexico,* II, 286.
9. Frances Parkinson Keyes, *The Grace of Guadalupe,* p. 29.
10. Rev. Charles Warren Currier, *History of Religious Orders,* p. 305.
11. *The Rule of St. Augustine,* p. 3.
12. Clement Raymond Orth, O.M.C., *The Approbation of Religious Institutes,* p. 50.
13. *Ibid.,* pp. 51-52.
14. Correspondence between parent Presentation Convent in Cork and Presentation Convent in San Francisco, California, dated December 5, 1955. Copy in Sisters of Mercy, Burlingame archives.
15. *Ibid.*
16. *Constitutions,* Congregation of the Sisters of the Presentation of the Ever Blessed Virgin Mary, San Francisco, 1936, p. 14.
17. Savage, *Mother McAuley,* p. 414.
18. *Ibid.*

19. Parenthouse archives, Dublin. Documented copy, Sisters of Mercy, Burlingame archives.
20. *Ibid.*
21. Documented material, Sisters of Mercy, Albany archives.
22. Quoted in Carroll, p. 377.
23. Parenthouse archives, Dublin. Documented copy, Burlingame archives.
24. Correspondence dated March 13, 1956, Burlingame archives.
25. Letter dated November 18, 1839.
26. Hartnett, p. 141.
27. Letter to Sister M. Angela written from Birr January 20, 1841.
28. Letter to Sister M. Frances August 5, 1840.
29. Letter to Sister M. Frances August 16, 1841.
30. Hartnett, p. 164.
31. *Rules and Constitutions,* Religious called Sisters of Mercy, 1872, pp. 3-4.
32. *Ibid.,* pp. 6-7.
33. *Ibid.,* p. 8.
34. *Retreat Instructions,* p. 159.
35. *The Hospital Almoner,* London, p. 26.
36. Letter to Sister M. Elizabeth at Kingstown July 27, 1837.
37. Hartnett, p. 57.
38. Sister M. Julian Baird, R.S.M., "Servants of the Sick," *Messenger of the Sacred Heart,* 92:5 (May, 1957), p. 39.
39. Hally Flack, "Nursing in Ireland from Pre-Christian Times to the Middle of the Nineteenth Century," *International Nursing Review,* VI:5 (September, 1931), p. 437.
40. Ralph H. Major, M.D., *A History of Medicine,* p. 681.
41. Logan Clendening, M.D., *Source Book of Medical History,* p. 499.
42. Carroll, pp. 156-57.

43. Hartnett, p. 88.
44. Murphy, p. 21.
45. William Howison, M.D., "Malignant Cholera in Ireland and Scotland," *Lancet,* November 10, 1832, pp. 203-204, 205.
46. Carroll, p. 190.
47. Limerick manuscript quoted in parenthouse "Cholera annals, p. 8.
48. *Dublin Evening Post,* December 19, 1832, in "Cholera annals," p. 5.
49. The story of the cholera, unless otherwise indicated, was summarized from the "Cholera Annals" Convent of Mercy, Carysfort Park, Blackrock, Co. Dublin, pp. 1-11.
50. Unpublished memoirs of Sister M. Clare Augustine Moore, documented copy, Albany archives.
51. Carroll, p. 447.
52. Crampton, Bart, F.R.S., "The Late Sir Philip Crampton," *Medical Times and Gazette* (London), XVI (June 18, 1858), 636-37.
53. Sir William Stokes [his son], William Stokes-Masters of Medicine, pp. 49-50.
54. James J. Walsh, *Makers of Modern Medicine,* p. 168.
55. Letter to Sister M. Frances from Galway, June 30, 1840.
56. Letter to Sister M. Elizabeth, July 28, 1840.
57. Letter to Sister M. Aloysius, July 31, 1841.
58. Letter to Sister M. Teresa, August 3, 1841.
59. Walsh, *Makers of Modern Medicine,* p. 205.
60. Letter to Sister Mary Teresa, December 13, 1836.
61. Walsh, *Makers of Modern Medicine,* p. 172.
62. *Annals,* I, 121.
63. Letter to Sister M. Aloysius, September 20, 1841.
64. Carroll, p. 437.
65. Hartnett, p. 56.
66. *Annals,* I, 56.

PART IV. A SPIRIT TESTED

1. Robert W. Habenstein and Edwin A. Christ, *Profession-alizer, Traditionalizer, and Utilizer,* p. 50.
2. J. E. O'Mahony (Father James, O.M.Cap.), "A Mission of Mercy," *Wherefore This Waste?* p. 125.
3. Rev. H. Collins, in Hartnett, p. 178.
4. Manuscript, Sisters of Mercy, Burlingame archives.
5. *Retreat Instructions,* p. 40.
6. Quoted in Rt. Rev. Hugh F. Blunt, *The Quality of Mercy,* p. 15.
7. D. Columba Marmion, *Words of Life,* p. 71.
8. Rev. Bede Jarrett, O.P., *Our Lady of Lourdes,* pp. 15-16.
9. Kinsale archives; *Familiar Instructions,* p. 144; Hartnett, pp. 55, 110.
10. Hartnett, p. 97.
11. Letter to Sister Mary Teresa White, November 1, 1838.
12. *Ibid.,* October 12, 1838.
13. Letter to Sister Mary Aloysius, September 24, 1841.
14. Letter to Sister Mary Angela, December 20, 1837.
15. Letter to Sister Mary Cecelia, January 18, 1841.
16. Letter to Sister Mary Teresa Purcell, early in 1841.
17. Letter to Sister Mary Elizabeth, July 28, 1840.
18. Inscribed manuscript on the "House of Mercy" undated but marked 6th of September, 1841, Albany archives documented copy.
19. Hartnett, p. 152.
20. *Familiar Instructions of Rev. Mother McAuley,* ed. Sisters of Mercy, St. Louis, Missouri, St. Louis: Ev. E. Carreras, 1888, p. 21.
21. *Rules and Constitutions,* p. 10.
22. *Ibid.*
23. James J. Walsh, "Portraits From the Past: Catherine M'Auley," *Trained Nurse and Hospital Review,* LXX:3 (March, 1923), p. 219.
24. Hartnett, p. 106.

25. Carroll, p. 383.
26. Inscribed manuscript on the "House of Mercy" undated but marked 6th of September, 1841, documented copy Albany archives.
27. *Rules and Constitutions,* pp. 8-9.
28. *Retreat Instructions,* p. 72.
29. *Familiar Instructions,* p. 18.
30. *Mercy Constitutions,* p. 10.
31. Sister M. Lourdine Cooke, R.S.M., "The Contributions of Mother Mary Catherine McAuley to the Social Betterment of Society," pp. 75-76. In the paragraph quoted the author gave credit to I. Smith, O.P., *St. Thomas Aquinas and Human Social Life* (Washington: Catholic University of America Press, 1945), p. 11.
32. *Familiar Instructions,* p. 18.
33. *Ibid.,* p. 20.
34. *Retreat Instructions,* p. 134.
35. *Ibid.*
36. Letter to Sister Mary Teresa White, October 12, 1838.
37. Letter to Sister Mary Elizabeth, July 24, 1839.
38. *Familiar Instructions,* p. 138.
39. O'Mahony (Father James, O.M.Cap.), pp. 130-31.
40. *Rules and Constitutions,* p. 10.
41. *Familiar Instructions,* pp. 16-18.
42. *Rules and Constitutions,* p. 11.
43. *Retreat Instructions,* p. 74.
44. *Ibid.,* p. 111.
45. *Familiar Instructions,* p. 142.
46. Ralph W. Tyler, "Educational Problems in Other Professions," *Education in Libraryship,* ed. Bernard R. Berelson, pp. 22-28.
47. Genevieve K. Bixler and Roy W. Bixler, "The Professional Status of Nursing," *The American Journal of Nursing,* XLV (September, 1945), 734.
48. Hartnett, p. 107.
49. Letter to Sister Mary Frances, inscribed August 4, 1841.
50. Sisters of Mercy of the Union, "Proceedings of the Third

Annual Institute in Hospital Administration and Nursing Education" (Cincinnati, 1950), p. 88.

51. *Rules and Constitutions,* pp. 7-8.
52. Carroll, p. 329.
53. Hartnett, pp. 113-14.
54. *Familiar Instructions,* pp. 78-80.
55. Hartnett, pp. 62-63.
56. Arthur R. McGratty, S.J., *The Sacred Heart Yesterday, Today and Tomorrow,* p. 197.
57. *Familiar Instructions,* p. 138.
58. *Rules and Constitutions,* p. 46.
59. *Familiar Instructions,* p. 86.
60. Joseph F. Gallen, S.J., "Renovation and Adaptation," *Review for Religious,* XIV, No. 6 (November, 1955), 295.
61. *Ibid.,* p. 302.
62. Pius XI, "Quadragesimo Anno" or "Reconstructing the Social Order," 1931, n. 79 in *Five Great Encyclicals* (New York: The Paulist Press, 1939).
63. The only source for the doctor's name which the present writer could find was the undocumented article by Baird, p. 39.
64. Murphy, pp. 11-12.
65. Fanny Tighe was the Foundress' earliest companion who left her, as the House on Baggot Street was nearing completion, to enter the Presentation Convent in Galway, but whose friendship continued through life.
66. Savage, *Catherine McAuley,* p. 57.
67. Sister Mary Hilda Miley, R.S.M., *The Ideals of Mother McAuley and Their Influence,* pp. 39-40.
68. M. T. Marnane, *A Guide for Catholic Teachers,* p. 48.
69. Sister Mary Vincent Hartnett, the Foundress' future biographer.
70. Letter to Sister Mary Anne, August 20, 1840.
71. *Ibid.*
72. Savage, *Catherine McAuley,* pp. 202-203.
73. Letter to Sister Mary Frances from Limerick, November 17, 1838.

74. Letter to Sister Mary Frances, November 30, 1840.
75. Savage, *Catherine McAuley,* p. 264.
76. *Retreat Instructions,* p. 162.
77. Hartnett, p. 91.
78. *Ibid.,* p. 97.
79. *Ibid.,* p. 72.
80. Sister Mary Finbarr McCready, H.H.M., "Mother Mary Catherine McAuley: Her Humility" (unpublished study, St. Louis University, April 1954), p. 2.
81. Letter to Sister M. Frances Warde, November 13, 1840. Original, Sisters of Mercy, Burlingame archives. The Foundress was referring to Father Matthew.

PART V. TO THE SOUND OF WAR

1. Shane Leslie, *Cardinal Manning, His Life and Labours,* p. 46.
2. Helen Louise Hammack, "The Work of the Sisters of Mercy in the Crimea and Its Reference to Modern Nursing," pp. 11-17.
3. *Ibid.,* p. 17.
4. *Annals,* Vol. II, p. 128.
5. Sister Mary Aloysius Doyle, *Memories of the Crimea,* p. 6.
6. *Ibid.,* p. 7.
7. *Annals,* II, 143. This was not the first contact which Sidney Herbert had with sisters. Through a charitable lady by the name of Mrs. Vershcoyle, Mr. Herbert had offered Mother McAuley the ground upon which to build the convent and school in Booterstown in 1838. (Cf. Barry, p. 53.) Yet more interesting is the fact that Sidney Herbert was the agent transacting the business for the Foundress' purchase of the ground on Baggot Street in 1824. (Cf. Barry, p. 26.)
8. Sister Marie Jeanne d'Arc Hughes, R.S.M., "Crimean Diary of Mother M. Francis Bridgman War Companion of Florence Nightingale," p. 4. This thesis published for

the first time many of the letters, documents, and experiences which Mother M. Francis Bridgeman had recorded on her return home. This unpublished manuscript entitled, "An Account of the Missions of the Sisters of Mercy in the Military Hospitals of the East," held in the archives of the Sisters of Mercy, Kinsale, Ireland, was not written with the intention of being published. Rather, the report was considered confidential and of a secret nature. Mother Bridgeman believed that her higher superiors should be fully aware of the facts recorded in the account in order to be guided in future circumstances. "It does not seem to have been written in an effort to vindicate her peculiar position, though it does just that, but rather with the thought of giving valuable aid to superiors, at some later date." Hughes, ii.

9. *Ibid.*, p. 6.
10. Doyle, p. 28.
11. Hammack, p. 22. Quotes from Lord Stanmore, *Sidney Herbert*, Vol. I, 370.
12. Doyle, p. 29. Galata was a suburb of Constantinople where the French Sisters of Charity of St. Vincent de Paul had a convent and school. Two of these sisters came by boat to the ship where Mother Bridgeman and her sisters were and welcomed them to the French convent on Eastern soil. It was Christmas Eve when they arrived; they left on the Feast of Holy Innocents. (Therapia was about eight miles from Constantinople on the Asiatic side of the Bosphorus.)
13. *Ibid.*, p. 39.
14. Hughes, p. 23.
15. Hammack, p. 50.
16. Hughes, pp. 24-25 quoting from Bridgeman, pp. 53-66.
17. Hammack, p. 53.
18. Fanny Taylor, *Eastern Hospitals and English Nurses*, p. 153.
19. *Ibid.*, pp. 154-55.

20. Lord Stanmore, *Sidney Herbert Lord Herbert of Lea,* p. 414.
21. Hughes, p. 56.
22. *Ibid.*
23. *Ibid.,* p. 57.
24. Some biographers attribute Miss Nightingale's semi-invalidism of later years to this illness.
25. Hughes, pp. 59-60.
26. *Ibid.,* pp. 70-80.
27. Doyle, p. 73.
28. Hughes, p. 103.
29. Doyle, p. 78.
30. Hammack, p. 85.
31. Hughes, p. 105.
32. *Ibid.,* pp. 106-107. The letter received by the Cardinal was sent by him to Mother Bridgeman on her return to Kinsale. Cf. Doyle, p. 105.
33. Hughes, pp. 114-15.
34. S. M. Mitra, *The Life and Letters of Sir John Hall,* pp. 450-51.
35. *Ibid.,* p. 456.
36. *Ibid.,* p. 458.
37. Hughes, p. 123.
38. Photostat copy Burlingame archives from original at Kinsale, Ireland.
39. *Ibid.*
40. *Annals, II,* 139, and Shane Leslie, "Forgotten Passages in the Life of Florence Nightingale," *Dublin Review,* No. 323 (October, 1917) pp. 194-95. The selections omitted in the Annals by ellipsis were supplied from Leslie's reference. Neither one was quoted in its entirety and for that reason one ellipsis had to be retained in the present work. Some authors quote a small section of this letter and attribute Miss Nightingale writing it of Mother Bridgeman, but this obviously is in error.
41. Stanmore, pp. 404-405.
42. *Ibid.,* p. 404.

43. Hughes, ii.
44. *Annals,* II, 212-15.
45. Leslie, *Cardinal Manning,* p. 49.
46. Exact year verified through correspondence with Mother M. Clare, London, July 2, 1957. Conflicting data exist as to the year of the bestowal of the Royal Red Cross. Cf. Leslie, "Forgotten Passages" p. 196.
47. Doyle, p. 128.
48. Incidents supplied from the local English annals by Mother M. Clare, London.
49. Original in the archives of the Sisters of Mercy, London; Hospital of St. John & St. Elizabeth.
50. *The Centenary Story of a Famous Hospital,* Hospital of St. John and St. Elizabeth 1856-1956, p. 9.

PART VI. ACCORDING TO THE PATTERN

1. Alphonse M. Schwitalla, S.J., "The Centenary of the Mercy Hospital, Pittsburgh," *Hospital Progress,* XXVIII, No. 4 (April, 1947), p. 97.
2. *Annals, III,* 259-60.
3. Ellen Ryan Jolly, LL.D., *Nuns of the Battlefield,* p. 227.
4. *Annals,* II, 147. The number of Sisters who went to Amiens is listed as three. (Cf. also Doyle, p. 13.)
5. *Annals,* II, 130.
6. *Annals* of the Mater Hospital, Dublin, p. 7.
7. *Ibid.,* p. 8.
8. The Honorable Judge Thomas O'Hagan, at a Board Meeting, February 18, 1867 quoted in *Annals* of the Mater Hospital, p. 13.
9. Walsh, *Makers of Modern Medicine,* p. 182.
10. Flack, p. 437.
11. Sister M. Aurelia McArdle, *California's Pioneer Sister of Mercy,* pp. 35-36.
12. *Ibid.,* p. 41.
13. *Ibid.,* pp. 59-60.

14. Edward Topham, M.D., *St. Mary's Hospital and the Sisters of Mercy,* pp. 5-6.
15. *Annals,* II, 220.
16. *Annual Report,* (1956), Hospital of St. John and St. Elizabeth, London, p. 13.
17. Figures were compiled from the 1957 Directory of the Catholic Hospital Association and the 1956 Directory of the American Hospital Association wherever possible. Some figures were obtained through correspondence.
18. Sister Mary Eulalia Herron, R.S.M., *The Sisters of Mercy in the United States,* p. 67.
19. *Annals* of the Mater Hospital, Dublin, p. 18.

EPILOGUE

1. Murphy, p. 23.
2. Carroll, p. 284.
3. *Rules and Constitutions,* pp. 9-10.

APPENDIX B

Table I—Compiled in large part from the 1957 Directory of the Catholic Hospital Association.

Where more than one school was established in the same year, the size of the school by enrollment was used as the order for listing.

Table II—Compiled from an official list of *Recognized Training Schools* published by the Irish BOARD OF NURSING.

APPENDIX C

Table III—Compiled in large part from the 1957 Directory of the Catholic Hospital Association.

Table IV—Compiled from the 1956 Irish Catholic Directory and from a list supplied by the Hospitals Commission of Dublin. (See note below.)

Table V—Compiled from data supplied the author by many persons through correspondence.

A DESCRIPTION OF IRELAND'S HEALTH SERVICE

Ireland has accomplished much recently in reorganizing its health service. In the last decade many improvements have been made in the dispensary service, and provision has been made for county clinics. In addition, the Department of Health maintains district, county, and regional hospitals. While the Sisters of Mercy have some of their own hospitals in Ireland they operate as well many of the above mentioned government institutions.

A description of Ireland's health service, both old and new, may be of benefit to those not familiar with the system, other than to associate it perhaps with the Irish Hospital Sweepstakes.

DISPENSARIES

There are 588 dispensary districts. Each district has at least one dispensary, and the larger districts include dispensary depots to cover the outlying areas. A part-time district medical officer holds regular hours for medical care of a general and minor nature for persons unable to pay for such care.

DISTRICT HOSPITALS

There are 56 district hospitals situated in the principal towns. Ordinarily, the district hospital is intended for acute medical, minor surgical, and normal obstetrical patients. Certain medical cases may need to be referred to the larger institutions.

COUNTY HOSPITALS

There are 24 county hospitals. These are centrally located in the counties and provide care for acute medical, major surgery, and complicated obstetrical cases. COUNTY HOMES accommodating the aged and infirm deal with chronic and long-term illness, and some care for obstetrical patients as well. The COUNTY CLINICS are integrated with the COUNTY HOSPITAL SYSTEM and wherever possible serve as an extended out-patient department.

REGIONAL HOSPITALS

There are regional hospitals in a few centrally located areas, chosen in relation to the surrounding counties and their proximity to medical centers. These are intended to cover a broad spectrum of specialized treatment and to act as research and teaching centers.

SPECIAL HOSPITALS

There are special hospitals located in regional and subregional areas to care for persons with conditions such as orthopedic, tuberculosis, cancer, communicable disease, and mental illness. Some of these conditions may however be treated also in the other types of hospitals.

BIBLIOGRAPHY

Andre, Marius. *Columbus*. Translated from the French by Eloise Parkhurst Huguenin. New York: Alfred A. Knopf, Inc., 1928.

Annals of the Mater Hospital, Dublin, Ireland.

Annals of the Sisters of Mercy, ed. Members of the Order of Mercy [Mother Teresa Austin Carroll].

    Vol. I: Ireland. New York: The Catholic Publication Society Co., 1881.

    Vol. II: England, At the Crimea, in Scotland, Australia, and New Zealand. New York: Catholic Publication Society Co., 1883.

    Vol. III: Newfoundland and the United States. New York: Catholic Publication Society Co., 1889.

    Vol. IV: South America, Central America, and the United States. New York: P. O'Shea, Publisher, 1895.

Annual Report (1956), Hospital of St. John and St. Elizabeth, London, England.

Baird, Sister M. Julian, R.S.M. "Servants of the Sick," *Messenger of the Sacred Heart*, XCII, No. 5 (May, 1957), 39-41.

Barker, Sister Rosanna, S.C. "Mother Margaret Cecilia George, First Superior of the Sisters of Charity of Cincinnati, O." Unpublished Master's thesis, St. Louis University, 1944.

Barry, K.M. *Catherine McAuley and the Sisters of Mercy,* Dublin: Fallon & Son, 1894.

Bell, Andrew. *Historical Sketches of Feudalism.* London: 1807.

Belloc, Bessie R. "Catherine McAuley," *Historic Nuns.* London: Duckworth & Co., 1898.

Bettany, G.T. *Eminent Doctors: Their Lives and Their Work.* Vol. II. London: John Hogg, Paternoster Row, 1885.

Bixler, Genevieve K. and Bixler, Roy W. "The Professional Status of Nursing." *The American Journal of Nursing,* XLV (September, 1945), 730-35.

Blunt, Rt. Rev. Hugh F. *The Quality of Mercy.* Milwaukee: Bruce Publishing Company, 1945.

Burton, Katherine. *So Surely Anchored.* New York: P. J. Kenedy & Sons, 1948.

Carroll, Mother Teresa Austin. *Life of Catherine McAuley.* St. Louis: The Vincentian Press, 1866.

"Catherine McAuley—the Heiress from Coolock," *Irish Independent,* December 12, 1955.

The Centenary Story of a Famous Hospital, Hospital of St. John and St. Elizabeth 1856-1956. London: Spenser Press, Ltd., 1956.

Clendening, Logan, M.D. (comp.). *Source Book of Medical History.* New York: Paul B. Hoeber, Inc., Medical Book Department of Harper & Brothers, 1942.

Code, Joseph B. "The Sisters of Mercy," *The Commonweal,* XV, No. 11 (January 13, 1932), 294-96.

Constitutions, Congregation of the Sisters of the Presentation of the Ever Blessed Virgin Mary. San Francisco, 1936.

Cook, Sir Edward. *The Life of Florence Nightingale*. New York: The Macmillan Company, 1942.

Cooke, Sister M. Lourdine, R.S.M. "The Contributions of Mother Mary Catherine McAuley to the Social Betterment of Society." Unpublished Master's dissertation, The Catholic University of America, Washington, D.C., 1948.

Crampton, Bart, F.R.S. "The Late Sir Philip Crampton," *Medical Times and Gazette* (London), XVI (June, 1858), 636-37.

Currier, Rev. Charles Warren. *History of Religious Orders*. New York: Murphy and McCarthy, Publishers, 1896.

Darras, J. E. *A General History of the Catholic Church*. Vol. III and IV. New York: P. O'Shea, Publisher, 1868.

De Madariaga, Salvador. *Christopher Columbus*. New York: The Macmillan Company, 1940.

Dock, Lavinia L. and Stewart, Isabel M. *A Short History of Nursing*. 4th ed. New York: G. P. Putnam's Sons, 1938.

Dolan, Albert H., O. Carm. *Matt Talbot, Alcoholic*. Chicago: The Carmelite Press, 1947.

Doyle, Sister M. Aloysius. *Memories of the Crimea*. London: Burns & Oates, Ltd., 1897.

Familiar Instructions of Rev. Mother McAuley. ed. Sisters of Mercy, St. Louis, Mo. St. Louis: Ev. E. Carreras, 1888.

Fitzwilliam, Charles William and Bourke, Richard (eds.). *Correspondence of the Right Honourable Edmund Burke*. Vol. IV. London: Francis and John Rivington, 1844.

Flack, Hally. "Nursing in Ireland from Pre-Christian Times to the Middle of the Nineteenth Century," *International Nursing Review*, VI, No. 5 (September, 1931), 428-41.

Footprints of Mercy, 1847-1947. Pittsburgh, Pennsylvania: Mercy Hospital.

Gallen, Joseph F., S.J. "Renovation and Adaptation," *Review for Religious*, XIV, No. 6 (November, 1955), 293-318.

Garrison, Fielding H. *An Introduction to the History of Medicine*. Philadelphia: W. B. Saunders Company, 1917.

Gwynn, J. Minor. *Curriculum Principles and Social Trends.* New York: The Macmillan Company, 1950.

Habenstein, Robert W. and Christ, Edwin A. *Professionalizer, Traditionalizer, and Utilizer.* Columbia: University of Missouri, 1955.

Hammack, Helen Louise. "The Work of the Sisters of Mercy in the Crimea and Its Reference to Modern Nursing." Unpublished Master's thesis, San Francisco College for Women, 1952.

Hammond, J. L. and Hammond, Barbara. *The Age of the Chartists.* London: Longmans, Green, and Co., 1930.

————. *The Town Labourer.* London: Longmans, Green, and Co., 1917.

Hartnett, Mother Mary Vincent. Memoirs: *Popular Life of Catherine McAuley.* ed. Sisters of Mercy, St. Louis, Mo. Baltimore: The Baltimore Publishing Co., 1887 and New York: P. J. Kenedy, Excelsior Catholic Publishing House, 1893.

Hayes, Carlton J. H. *A Political and Social History of Modern Europe.* I, New York: The Macmillan Company, 1931.

Healy, E. Nellie. "Some Glimpses of Life in Ancient Ireland," *International Nursing Review,* VI, No. 3 (May, 1931), 233-38.

Herron, Sister Mary Eulalia, R.S.M. *The Sisters of Mercy in the United States 1843-1928.* New York: The Macmillan Company, 1929.

Hoever, Hugo, S.O. Cist., ed. "St. Peter Nolasco," *Lives of the Saints.* New York: Catholic Book Publishing Co., 1955.

The Hospital Almoner. Prepared by a Committee of the Hospital Almoners' Association. London: George Allen and Unwin, Ltd., 1935.

Hospital Directory. A Report published as Part II of *Hospital Progress,* Vol. XXXVIII, No. 2 (February, 1957). St. Louis: Catholic Hospital Association, 1957.

Hospital Guide. A Listing published as Part Two of *Hospi-*

tals, (August 1, 1956). Chicago: American Hospital Association, 1956.

Howison, William, M.D., "Malignant Cholera in Ireland and Scotland," *Lancet,* November 10, 1832, pp. 203-207.

Hughes, Sister Marie Jeanne d'Arc, R.S.M. "Crimean Diary of Mother M. Francis Bridgman War Companion of Florence Nightingale 1854-1856," Unpublished Master's dissertation, The Catholic University of America, 1948.

Ireland's Hospitals. eds. J. O'Sheehan and E. de Barra. Dublin: Hospital Trust, Ltd., 1956.

Irish Catholic Directory and Almanac. Dublin: James Duffy & Co., Ltd., 1956.

Jarrett, Rev. Bede, O.P. *Our Lady of Lourdes.* Westminster, Maryland: The Salve Regina—Newman Bookshop, 1945.

Jolly, Ellen Ryan, LL.D. *Nuns of the Battlefield.* 4th ed. Providence, Rhode Island: The Providence Visitor Press, 1930.

Keyes, Frances Parkinson. *The Grace of Guadalupe.* New York: Julian Messner, Inc., 1941.

Knight, Arthur George, S.J. *The Life of Christopher Columbus.* London: Burns and Oates, 1877.

Lennon, Sister Mary Isidore, R.S.M. *Mother Catherine McAuley A Great Social Worker.* St. Louis: Sisters of Mercy of the Union, 1954.

Leslie, Shane. *Cardinal Manning His Life and Labours.* New York: P. J. Kenedy & Sons, 1954.

————. "Forgotten Passages in the Life of Florence Nightingale," *Dublin Review,* No. 323 (October, 1917), pp. 179-98.

McArdle, Sister M. Aurelia, S.M. *California's Pioneer Sister of Mercy.* Fresno: Academy Library Guild, 1954.

McConomy, Sister M. Louis, R.S.M. *The Spirit of Mary Catherine McAuley.* Oklahoma City: Mt. St. Mary's Academy, 1922.

McCready, Sister Mary Finbarr, H.H.M. "Mother Mary Catherine McAuley: Her Humility," Unpublished study, St. Louis University, 1954.

McGratty, Arthur R., S.J. *The Sacred Heart Yesterday, Today and Tomorrow*. Chicago: Benziger Brothers, Inc., 1951.

McHugh, H. A., D.C.L. "The Making of a Mother's Heart," *The Redemptorist Record*, XIX: No. 6 (November-December, 1955), 175-77.

Major, Ralph H., M.D. *A History of Medicine*. Springfield, Illinois: Charles Thomas, Publisher, 1954.

Maloney, Sister Mary Berenice, S.M. comp. *Catherine McAuley, Foundress of the Sisters of Mercy and Her Apostolate the Care of the Sick*. Buffalo: Sisters of Mercy, 1955.

Marmion, D. Columba. *Words of Life*. ed. Dom Thibaut, O.S.B. St. Louis: B. Herder Book Co., 1952.

Marnane, M. T. *A Guide for Catholic Teachers*. New York: McMullen Books, Inc., 1952.

Member of the Order of Mercy. *Mother Mary Catherine McAuley*. New York: D. and J. Sadlier & Co., 1866.

Miley, Sister Mary Hilda, R.S.M. *The Ideals of Mother McAuley and Their Influence*. New York: P. J. Kenedy & Sons, 1931.

Mitra, S. M. *The Life and Letters of Sir John Hall*. London: Longmans, Green and Co., 1911.

Morison, Samuel Eliot. *Admiral of the Ocean Sea*. Boston: Little, Brown and Company, 1942.

Morley, John. ed. *Burke: English Men of Letters*. New York: Harper and Brothers, n. d.

Mullaly, Charles J., S.J. "The Spirit of Mother Mary Catherine McAuley," *Messenger of the Sacred Heart*, LXXII, No. 4 (April, 1937), 37-39.

Murphy, Rev. Dominic. "The Order of Mercy and Its Foundress," *Dublin Review*, XXII, No. 13 (March, 1847), 1-25.

"Nuns' Home Coming," *The Standard* (Dublin), October 7, 1955.

O'Mahony, J. E. (Father James, O. M. Cap.). "A Mission of Mercy," *Wherefore This Waste?* London: Burns, Oates and Washbourne, Ltd., 1936.

Orth, Clement Raymond, O.M.C. *The Approbation of Religious Institutes.* Washington, D.C.: The Catholic University of America, 1931.

Peter of St. Cecelio, Rev., O.D.M. *Annales Del Orden De Descalcos De N. S. De La Merced.* Barcelona: Dionisio Hidalgo, 1669.

Pius XI, Pope. "Quadragesimo Anno," or "Reconstruction of the Social Order," *Five Great Encyclicals.* New York: The Paulist Press, 1939.

Powers, Rev. James M. "Is Mother McAuley a Saint?" reprinted from *The Ecclesiastical Review,* May, 1935 (Philadelphia: The Dolphin Press), pp. 2-8.

Prescott, William H. *History of the Conquest of Mexico.* Vol. II. New York: John W. Lovell Company, 1843 preface.

———. *Ferdinand and Isabella.* Vol. II. New York: Harper & Brothers, Publishers, 1852.

Report of the Department of Health 1952-1953. Dublin: Stationery Office.

Retreat Instructions of Mother Mary Catherine McAuley. comp. Sister Mary Teresa Purcell. Edited by Sisters of Mercy, Albany, New York. Westminster, Maryland: The Newman Press, 1952.

The Rule of St. Augustine. New York: The Catholic Publication Society Co., From the Dublin edition, n.d.

Rules and Constitutions, Religious called Sisters of Mercy. Dublin: J. M. O'Toole and Son, 1872.

Ryan, E. A., S.J. "The Sisters of Mercy: An Important Chapter in Church History," *Theological Studies,* Vol. 18, No. 2 (June, 1957), 254-70.

Savage, Roland Burke, S.J. *Catherine McAuley, The First Sister of Mercy.* Dublin: M. H. Gill and Son, Ltd., 1949.

———. *A Valiant Dublin Woman: The Story of George's Hill.* Dublin: M. H. Gill and Son, Ltd., 1940.

Schwitalla, Alphonse M., S.J. "The Centenary of the Mercy Hospital, Pittsburgh," *Hospital Progress,* XXVIII, No. 4 (April, 1947), 97-103.

Simon, Sister Mary of the Angels, R.S.M. *One Life in Christ.* New York: P. J. Kenedy & Sons, 1940.

Sister of Mercy, "Mercy Girdles the Earth," *The Standard* (Dublin), January 6, 1956.

Sisters of Mercy, Albany, New York archives. Collection of letters of Mother Mary Catherine McAuley and other primary source material.

Sisters of Mercy, Burlingame, California archives. Kinsale annals. Manuscript copy of the *Rules and Constitutions* of the Sisters of Mercy. Letter and prayer of Mother McAuley. Correspondence.

Sisters of Mercy, Carysfort Park, Blackrock, Co. Dublin archives. Correspondence, unpublished memoirs of Sister M. Clare Augustine Moore and Mother M. Clare Moore, Cholera annals.

Sisters of Mercy, Mater Misericordia Hospital, Dublin annals.

Sisters of Mercy of the Union of the United States of America. "Proceedings of the Third Annual Institute in Hospital Administration and Nursing Education," Cincinnati: The Sisters of Mercy, 1950.

Smith, Mary Constance. A *Sheaf of Golden Years 1856-1906.* New York: Benziger Brothers, 1906.

Stanmore, Lord. *Sidney Herbert Lord Herbert of Lea.* Vol. I. London: John Murray, 1906.

Stokes, Sir William. *William Stokes: Masters of Medicine.* London: T. Fisher Unwin, 1898.

[Taylor, Fanny] A Lady Volunteer. *Eastern Hospitals and English Nurses.* 3rd ed. rev. London: Hurst and Blackett, 1857.

Tertiary of the Order. *Our Lady's Order of Ransom Called Mercy.* Portland, Maine: The Coughlan Press, 1934.

Thomas Aquinas, Sister M., O.P., M.A. and Synon, Mary. *This is Our Heritage.* Boston, Ginn and Company, 1943.

Thurston, Herbert, S.J. "Saint Peter Nolasco," *Butler's Lives of the Saints.* Vol. I. New York: P. J. Kenedy and Sons, 1925.

Tooley, Sarah A. *The Life of Florence Nightingale.* New York: The Macmillan Company, 1905.

Topham, Edward, M. D. *St. Mary's Hospital and the Sisters of Mercy.* San Francisco: By the author, 1950.

Tyler, Ralph W. "Educational Problems in Other Professions," *Education for Librarianship.* Edited by Bernard R. Berelson. Chicago: American Library Association, 1949.

Walsh, James J., M.D. *The History of Nursing.* New York: P. J. Kenedy & Sons, 1929.

———. *Makers of Modern Medicine.* New York: Fordham University Press, 1907.

———. "Portraits From the Past: Catherine M'Auley," *Trained Nurse and Hospital Review,* LXX, No. 3 (March, 1923), 218-20.

———. *These Splendid Sisters.* New York: J. H. Sears & Company, Inc., 1927.

———. *The World's Debt to the Irish.* Boston: The Stratford Company, 1926.

Walsh, William Thomas. *Isabella of Spain.* New York: Robert M. McBride & Company, 1930.

Ward, Rt. Rev. E. C. *The Foundress of the Sisters of Mercy.* Dublin: Convent of the Mother of Mercy, 1956.

White, Alban. *Matt Talbot A Christian Hero.* Cork: The Forum Press, 1944.

Wiley, Sister Mary Louise, R.S.M. "A Survey in Religion and Religious Activities in Basic Schools of Nursing Conducted by the Sisters of Mercy of the Union in the United States." Unpublished Master's dissertation, The Catholic University of America, 1951.

Woodham-Smith, Cecil. *Florence Nightingale.* New York: McGraw Hill Book Company, 1951.

The Works of the Right Honorable Edmund Burke. Vol. IV. 2d ed. revised. Boston: Little, Brown and Company, 1866.

INDEX

Aikenhead, Mother Mary, and the Irish Sisters of Charity, 27, 28, 49, 57

Aloysius, Sister Mary; see Doyle

Armstrong, Reverend Father Edward, 25, 28, 54

Armstrong, William, 22-23, 54

Balaclava, 100, 101, 112

Bell, Andrew, 17

Benedict XIII, Pope, issues Bull *Pretiosus* in 1727, 46

Benedict XIV, Pope, issues Constitution *Quamvis Justo* in 1794, 47

Bermondsey Convent of Sisters of Mercy, 34; Mother M. Clare Moore, superior, 35; first public religious ceremony in England since the Reformation, 35

Blake, Reverend Michael, 25 ff.

Blake, William, concern over plight of children, 13

Bridgeman, Mother M. Frances: sends sisters on California mission, 93-94; confirmed by War Office as Superior of second group of Sisters of Mercy to go to the Crimea, 94; accepts hospitality of Sisters of Charity at Galata, 95; goes to General Hospital at Scutari, 95; describes sadness of her plight there, 95; goes to the Koulali Barrack Hospital, 96; document drawn up declaring her Superior of the sisters from Ireland, 97; named Superintendent of the Koulali General Hospital, 96; continues as such with the approval of Miss Hutton and Lord Paulett, 99; arrival at Balaclava, 101; welcomed by Dr. Hall and named Superintendent of the General Hospital at Balaclava, 101; interviews with Miss Nightingale, 105; submits resignation to Dr. Hall, 105; explains methods of nursing of the sisters to Miss Nightingale, 106; trip home, 107 ff.

Burke, Edmund, 15, 16

Callaghan, William, 23 ff., 54

Care of sick in their homes, 27, 54, 121-22

Catholic Emancipation, 16

Catholic Relief Act, 16, 18

Charity Infirmary on Jervis Street, 115-16, 147

Cheyne, Dr. John, 60, 64

Chicago, arrival of Sisters of Mercy, 114

Child labor, 13

Chimney sweepers, 13, 28

Cholera, Asiatic: Balaclava, 101; Chicago, 114; Dublin, 57 ff.; San Francisco, 116 ff.; Scutari, 95; Townsend Street Hospital, 57; treatment used, 57-58

Civil War, nursing of the Sisters of Mercy, 91

Clare, Sister Mary; see Moore

Codrington, General Sir William J., 104, 106-107

Colles, Dr. Abraham, 56, 61

A WAY
OF MERCY

Catherine McAuley's
Contribution
to Nursing

by

SISTER MARY BEATA BAUMAN,
Sister of Mercy

"*We have ever confided largely in Divine Providence and shall continue to do so.*"

In this faith Catherine McAuley devoted a lifetime of service to nursing God's poor . . . and founding the second largest congregation of women in the Catholic Church — the Sisters of Mercy.

Against the background of turbulence in Ireland — 1778-1841 — Sister Mary Beata Bauman unfolds the story of a dedicated woman and her good works, a woman who, beginning as a benevolent secular lady going about merciful errands in a simple costume of black, moved forward to become foundress of a world-wide order now believed to number at least 30,000.

The first woman, since the Reformation, permitted (under religious auspices) to enter the public hospitals of the United Kingdom to care for the sick, Catherine McAuley was born near Dublin in 1778. In her youth she learned much of nursing by caring for those she loved — and associating with medical men. "She knew comfortable circumstances, poverty, and wealth;

(Continued on back flap)